Raising Goats

Meat - Dairy - Fibre

By Felicity Stockwell

ISBN 978 1 90487 1675
A catalogue record for this book is available from
the British Library.

Published by
The Good Life Press Ltd.
PO Box 536
Preston
PR2 9ZY

www.goodlifepress.co.uk
www.homefarmer.co.uk

Set by The Good Life Press Ltd.
Photographs by Felicity Stockwell
Cover designed by Rachel Gledhill
Printed and bound in Great Britain

CONTENTS

RAISING GOATS
DAIRY - MEAT - FIBRE

By Felicity Stockwell

Foreword

The one thing that is certain with keeping animals of any kind, be they pets or domestic servants, is that you will only get out of them as much as you put in. I have always treated my animals and my children with the same psychology: love, care and reasonable demands. Animals, like children, should be a pleasure to have around.

With regard to the general husbandry of keeping goats in the 21st Century, the rules and regulations are a world apart from the time when I first set out on my caprine adventures in the early 1970s. So much has changed in so very many ways. Foot and Mouth Disease and Bluetongue are just two of the ailments for which the modern day goat keeper must be vigilant and gone are the days when you could transport your goat in the back of the family car! This book sets out to help you choose, enjoy and get the very best out of your goats, whether they are for pleasure, domestic use or a small commercial enterprise. I hope that this book serves as a general practical point of reference to help you to achieve health and happiness for your goats, your family and yourself.

About the Author

Felicity Stockwell has many years experience in keeping all forms of domestic livestock. Her first inspiration for keeping goats was fostered in the late 1950s while visiting Guernsey as a child and being enchanted by the beautiful golden goat which took its name from the island. Her origins are equine but, during the early 1970s whilst raising a large family of six children in rural Bedfordshire, she purchased her first goat with the proceeds of one week's secretarial temping for her husband's employers. With the princely sum of £25 she purchased Katy, a diminutive Saanen doe and the rest, as they say, is history! More recently and currently,

RAISING GOATS

she writes regular husbandry articles for a well known smallholding magazine. She has run her own commercial goat herd and now, retired to North Cornwall, has returned to her equestrian roots keeping and showing Exmoor ponies, sheep and goats and poultry.

CHAPTER ONE

THE LEGALITIES OF GOAT KEEPING – WHAT EVERY GOAT KEEPER SHOULD KNOW

In this world of rules, regulations and litigation, whatever project in life you are undertaking or about to undertake, being sure of your legal ground is essential.

Goat keeping is no exception and whether it is your intention to be a hobbyist or a professional producer, there are certain things you must be aware of for your own legal safety and that of others around you.

COUNTY PARISH HOLDING (CPH) NUMBER

Before you can keep or move any cloven-hoofed domesticated livestock onto your property (ie. sheep, goats, pigs or cows) you must obtain a CPH number. This allows Defra (now The Department for the Environment, Food and Rural Affairs but formerly the Department of Fisheries, Food, and Animal Health) to monitor the movement of livestock on or off your holding and to keep you informed and up to date with current animal legislation and health issues. It is a vital part of ensuring that the National Flock, in other words the entire population of farm animals, stays safe from real and sudden danger such as the Foot and Mouth epidemic of 2001 and more recently Bluetongue. With global warming occurring worldwide we could also see the spread of previously unknown diseases into more temperate regions of the world spread from hotter climates such as African Horse Sickness which affects a number of species.

It is illegal to keep goats without a CPH number, even if they are pets! There are financial penalties for those that flout this regulation and the risk of having your animals taken away.

Application is easy, even if you have a back garden with a goat shed in it. Apply by telephone to The Rural Payments Agency (RPA) on 0845 6037777 or go to the Defra website at www.defra.gov.uk where you will

RAISING GOATS

also find additional information. You will be able to make the application by phone and within a few days will receive a form with your number. It's that simple!

You will also need a Herd/Flock Number. This is the number that identifies your flock regardless of whether it consists of 2 goats or 250. All kids born on your holding will have an individual identity number and a UK flock number and this will be shown on their ear tag/s. Even if you do not plan to breed from your goats you will still need this ID number.

Your Herd/Flock Number can be obtained from the Animal Health Office which is another government agency, but this time a veterinary one. Details of your local Animal Health Office can be obtained at the same time as applying for your CPH number.

So now you are 'legal' and you can move your goats to your home.

ANIMAL MOVEMENTS

When you purchase your first goats the seller will provide all the necessary Movement Documents for you which will consist of 4 sheets of paper in different colours. These will clearly indicate where signatures or information are required and what you should do with each piece. It sounds complicated but it really isn't. Like most things in life, once done it is never forgotten! I will doubtless repeat this phrase throughout this book.

From your own perspective, once your Holding Number and Herd/Flock number have been issued you will receive a supply of Movement Documents from the appropriate agency for future use, should you want to move your livestock.

IDENTIFICATION AND EAR TAGGING

From 31st December 2009 all sheep and goats MUST, by law, have an electronic ear tag (EID) and if they are to be kept beyond 12 months of age or likely to leave your holding before that age, it must have TWO identical tags (one in each ear) The second tag does not have to be an EID tag but it must carry the same information.

The only differences between an EID tag and a normal plastic tag is that the information that is printed on the tag is also contained in a microchip within the tag. The cost of this is, of course, greater.

On average a standard tag costs from around 15 to 40p depending on type and an EID tag costs between 75p and £2.50, again depending on type. My own preference for goats is a small round 'button' tag which can be obtained from a number of outlets online. Personally I use Fearings (www.fearings.co.uk) who offer an excellent service to small volume keepers and will advise regarding current legislation and what you can have/should have embedded on your tags. They are also able to explain what you should do if your goat loses a tag and needs a replacement and the variations on a theme that you can opt for with the design of your tags.

Goats born before december 2009 will NOT need any more tags applied to them so don't panic if you go to buy a goat born before this date and find that it only has one tag, no EID tag or perhaps no tags at all. Any older goat may simply have an ear tattoo which can only be seen by shining a torch through the ear and comprises a series of dots which make up letters and numbers.

When moving such goats it is important to copy this ID onto the Movement Form if they are to travel. The Movement form described earlier is self explanatory in this respect.

KEEPING ACCURATE RECORDS

The keeping of accurate and up to date records of your goats is as important legally as it is for you as a point of reference. You will need a Holding Register. This is normally provided for you but if it doesn't automatically turn up after you have registered your Holding it can be obtained by contacting the Animal Movements department of your local Trading Standards Office by telephone. Just call your local County Council offices and ask to be transferred.

RAISING GOATS

In this self-explanatory register you will keep a record of the numbers of livestock you keep and their identification numbers (Ermintrude and Daisy simply won't do!). Personally I do add their names alongside as it aids my own identification and raises a smile if your register ever gets looked at by an Inspector (and yes, this occasionally does happens, so be warned!). It allows you to show movements on and off the holding, births, deaths and movements to slaughter, It is the diary of your animals' lives.

You will also need a Veterinary Medicine Records Book. This too is often provided but if not you can request one and, should the need arise, you can buy one for a couple of pounds from a smallholder supplies store or online from a variety of sources.

In this register you will need to keep records of what veterinary medicine you use, who supplied it, batch numbers, meat/milk withdrawal times and who administered the product and why. It is an invaluable reference for yourself too in order to accurately administer wormers and vaccinations. It can also be a valuable reference resource if you have a problem with your animals, both for yourself and your vet.

AND THE PURPOSE OF ALL THIS?

Some may feel that all this record keeping is a total waste of time and resources and that life jogged along quite happily in bygone years without all of this, but be assured that it is not a waste of time and that the agencies that enforce this legislation are neither nannying nor spying on us.

Fifty years ago we were a much smaller and insular nation. Our animals were rarely shipped all over the world and only travelled infrequently in any numbers on road transport. We killed the vast majority of our animals close to home for food and diseases which were around then were therefore largely isolated to the regions where they originated due to less movement, both across the country and the world.

Our lives today have changed beyond all recognition and in many cases so have those of the animals we keep. Legislation is there to protect the National Flock and to ensure that the UK remains a food producing nation and that all virulent disease is tracked and controlled at the very earliest opportunity, As small time goat keepers we represent a significant risk to the National Flock if we fail to observe these regulations and legislation that is there to protect us all in a changing world. My advice to you is to stay ahead of the legislation and be able to quote it Chapter and Verse to those that might challenge you.

FOOD CHAIN REGULATIONS

Here we move into a very different area with regard to what you do with products for consumption from your goats and any plans you may have to sell it to others.

PROVIDING MEAT FOR YOUR FAMILY

So long as your goats are slaughtered in an approved abattoir and transported subject to movement regulations you can legally feed your own family.

PROVIDING DAIRY PRODUCTS FOR YOUR FAMILY

All dairy products consumed by you do not require any approvals but legislation requires that ALL dairy products consumed by your family and friends must have received Food Hygiene and Dairy Hygiene approval from both the Environmental Health and Food Standards Agency. This is examined in more detail in Chapter 5.

So legally you cannot provide your family with goat's milk, yoghurt or cheese, unless you have fulfilled these requirements. The reality is that people do BUT, looking at the worst case scenario, if one of your family members or friends becomes ill and is hospitalised as a result of consuming your products, there is a possibility that you could be investigated and legal action taken against you. If this involved someone dying as a result you could find yourself a victim of the Criminal Justice system. I do not know of a case such as this happening but it could, so beware!

RAISING GOATS

MOVING ANIMALS TO SLAUGHTER

Current regulations demand that your goat/s are moved to slaughter in an appropriate vehicle. This means a trailer or livestock lorry that has a steel or steel lined floor and loading gates. Some people will have a suitable trailer for this purpose such as the Ifor Williams P6E, but if not then most small abattoirs will provide a collection service which will fulfil the above criteria for which a small charge of between £5 and £10 may be made depending on the distance and the number of animals. This topic is explored further in Chapter 6.

CURING OR SENDING YOUR SKINS FOR CURING

You can legally cure your own skins for personal use. You will have to collect them from the abattoir by prior arrangement and will require a Movement Form to accompany them in most cases as they legally represent a 'biological hazard.' Likewise, if you are collecting them for processing elsewhere then Movement Forms will need to accompany them. This is covered in more detail in Chapter 5.

INSURANCE LIABILITY

Many goat keepers will not bother with any insurance cover at all. My advice is to obtain at least third Party cover if possible. If you are providing products for resale it is essential, though not actually obligatory, to obtain Product Liability cover. I regard Product Liability cover as ABSOLUTELY essential. If you have the misfortune to have a claim made against you (and this can be something as small as a goat hair in the yoghurt!) it may become a costly affair. We live in a world were litigation rules and unfortunately there are many people who will take advantage of any situation they can, even if it is just to get some free products.

If you are selling your products via a Farmers' Market there are very reasonable Farmer's Market/Local Market Insurances available which your Market Organiser will be able to advise you about.

If you are running a goat product producing business from your home, however small, then you must also inform your Home contents/Building Insurance company of your activities or proposed activities or it can void your home insurance. Similarly, if you use your family vehicle to transport goods to markets and other outlets, your car insurers should also be informed. It will probably make a minimal impact on your insurance premium. If your premiums leap, then seek out new insurance with a smallholder friendly company such as the NFU.

NOISE, NUISANCE AND ODOUR

"But my goats don't smell!!" I hear you say. Well to you they don't but maybe to others they do. This can be particularly true if you own a Billy Goat (or buck). Much will depend on where you live and how close your property is to those of others. Theoretically, subject to the CPH number being obtained - and they don't ask how big your garden is - you can keep any livestock in your garden subject to local byelaws, BUT if they create a nuisance to others either by smell, noise or other means, you will be made to remove them by the Environmental Health Department. Basically we can all enjoy our own space so long as it is not detrimental to others in the enjoyment of their own. You will need to think this through carefully as it is always better to get it right from the beginning!

I once lived in a place where I was in close proximity to neighbours despite having 5 acres. I had over 60 goats at the time including a buck. I always kept them very clean and the buck was kept as far away from dwellings as possible. It worked particularly well as my next door neighbour kept an aviary full of parrots including Scarlet Macaws which are not known for their beautiful dawn chorus! As my milking machine was also going at full belt at the same time nobody bothered each other and it actually worked out very well, but think your circumstances through before you begin and perhaps talk to your neighbours about it. But do remember that there can be no bartering of goat products without the necessary permissions!

LOCAL BYELAWS AND YOUR PROPERTY

Before you begin to keep goats in your garden or on your land check

RAISING GOATS

any local byelaws regarding the keeping of livestock. If you own or have a mortgaged home then your solicitor will be able to tell you if there is anything in your deeds which precludes the keeping of non-domestic livestock. If your home is rented then consultation with your landlord will certainly be essential.

FENCING AND CONTAINMENT

As a livestock keeper it is your legal responsibility to ensure that you provide a secure environment for your goats. This includes stock proof fencing which will ensure your goats stay on your own property and cannot access adjoining property owners' crops and belongings. Although Third Party Liability insurance might cover you the first time your goats escape, it probably won't the next time, so it's worthwhile getting it right the first time. It is also in your best interests to keep predators such as dogs out. Foxes can also prey on young kids. A good stock proof fence is probably the best single investment you will ever make and if that can be backed up with an electric outrigger, then so much the better.

ANIMAL WELFARE ACT

The Animal Welfare Act is a fairly recent piece of legislation which aims to reduce neglect in all animals, both domestic and agricultural. It states that animals should be kept appropriately, fed adequately, have access to clean water at all times and be regularly checked at the very least daily. It is probably one of the best pieces of legislation conceived for the protection of animals in the last half century. The bottom line is that if you don't want the daily responsibility, then don't do it!

CHAPTER TWO

BUYING AND KEEPING GOATS FOR THE MODERN FAMILY

WHERE TO START.........

WHY A GOAT?

There could be a number of reasons why you are considering goat keeping. Perhaps you have some land and would like to provide milk, dairy products and perhaps meat for your family. Perhaps you just want one for a pet or you are or may become a hand spinner. Perhaps you do not have enough land for a cow or you may have lactose intolerance and want goat's milk , yoghurt and cheese. You might simply love goats!

HOW MANY SHOULD I KEEP?

Goats are herd animals and as such are not happy when kept alone, so you should always have two goats as an absolute minimum. This could take a variety of forms.

- ❋ A milking goat and her goatling daughter or wethered (castrated) son
- ❋ A pair of milking goats
- ❋ 2 wethers (for pets or meat production)
- ❋ 2 wethered Angoras for fleeces only
- ❋ A dairy goat and another variety such as an Angora or Pygmy.

This would work well if space is at a premium or if you want a goat for dairying and a goat for fibre. The permutations are actually almost endless and you will need to assess what your requirements are for your own smallholding or garden.

WHAT WOULD BE THE IDEAL SMALLHOLDER MIX?

If I could only keep 2 goats then my choice would be a nice dairy goat with proven milking performance, ideally aged between 3 and 7 years old and an Angora doe between 2 and 7 years old. These are the reasons why.....

The dairy goat will be able to fulfil your dairying needs, providing she has kidded in the last 12 months and been regularly milked.

The Angora would provide you with a shearing twice a year and will probably yield about 4 to 6kg of fleece which will enable you to spin up to 100 x 50g balls of wool. My reason for saying 'up to' is because the quantity will depend on the quality of the fleece.

Every autumn you will be able to mate your two goats to the same buck and, regardless of breed (with the exception of pygmies) the two goats will then provide you with up to four kids for the freezer. Angora crossed with some of the larger dairy breeds make very good carcasses as they tend to be less leggy and have good thighs and shoulders.

Crossbred goats showing hybrid vigour

Alternatively, you could choose an Angora buck one year and a dairy breed the following year. That way you would breed pure Angora one year and pure dairy breed the following year, but still have some hybrid kids for meat production. Of course there is no reason why a pure bred goat of any kind shouldn't be used for meat but cross breeding produces a hybrid vigour and with that comes size. An Angora cross is unlikely to become a viable milking animal so

RAISING GOATS

you should consider any Angora crossbreed as a companion animal or meat goat. The same applies in most cases to a Boer cross goat. A Boer goat is the ultimate goat for meat and is bred for this purpose. Always consider its offspring as meat, not dairy animals. Occasionally a Boer cross dairy breed will produce a kid with genetic faults, typically 'fish tail' or double teats which are impossible to milk anyway. This condition is covered in Chapter 7.

Age is important and 3 to 7 years of age will give you a mature animal that will already have kidded successfully, so you will know she is fertile and has kidded without serious problems. The fleece of a fibre goat will also still be good enough for home spinning between those ages.

WHAT BREED FOR DAIRYING?

Many people will tell you that certain goats are better for dairying than others because the butterfat content of milk varies from breed to breed. The latter part of that statement is true, but for the average family any breed of dairy goat will suffice. It is mainly down to you as to the type of goat you prefer and perhaps what is available within a reasonable radius of your holding. If you are   thinking of commercial goat keeping then this is a different matter because yield is vital.

A dairy goat from good milk lines will produce up to a gallon of milk a day. The average dairy goat will produce about 6 pints a day in her first year of milking, reducing to 3 to 4 pints a day in her second year. Milked regularly and kept warm in winter, she will continue to provide milk for up to 3 years without being mated, but there is no reason why you should not breed from her annually if you want to.

Golden Guernsey goats

Some breeds will not milk so well in the winter. This is particularly true of the Anglo-Nubian which dislikes the cold and will often drop milk yield in winter. Once the yield diminishes it is unlikely that it will return.

Smaller breeds such as the Golden Guernsey or English Guernsey are a delightful and rather sensitive goat and will serve a family well, but will not produce enough for the commercial dairy and their

Saanen

small frame also means they are less suitable for meat and indeed, given the fact that they are at risk, the female kids should not be considered for meat production unless they have faults.

Toggenburg goat

Saanen and British Saanen are much bigger goats and produce a good milk supply and a good meat carcass, particularly when crossed with other breeds. The majority of dairy producing goat herds in the UK now comprise of this breed.

The Toggenburg and Alpine goats are generally known as 'Swiss' goats and are very attractive, conjuring up scenes of Heidi. In my experience they are good dairy goats with nice temperaments and a compact body which again makes them very suitable for out crossing for meat. The British Toggenburg is a slightly different build of goat to her Toggenburg cousin, usually having a longer coat at the shoulder and thighs. These differences are important in the show ring but have little importance for the domesticated smallholder's goat.

Pygmy goats should only be considered as pets. They are not dairy goats, needing their milk for their own offspring and, in the UK at least, are not normally eaten! They are great companion animals, full of beans and quite delightful, but other than keeping your grass down and giving you hours of entertainment, that is where it ends. They do, of course, require the same degree of care and attention as any of the other breeds, other than the milking.

British Alpine goat

Pygmy goats

BREEDS FOR COMPANION ANIMALS

Unquestionably there will always be people who want goats purely for companionship and indeed, any goat other than an entire male (buck/ Billy goat) will do this very well. However, some are breed specific and in particular the Pygmy goat will fulfil this criteria. It is a tiny

goat, making it possible to keep a small group, even in a garden area. As pets, all males should be castrated or they will proliferate at a most alarming rate. Despite being companion animals, the legalities and regulations of goat keeping still apply to Pygmy goats in every way.

FIBRE GOATS

These goats fall into three categories: Angora, Cashmere and Cashgora. Cashmere goats are a specific breed, although crossbred Angoras are often referred to as such. Cashmere Goats are normally free ranging semi-feral goats. They have swept back horns, similar to all feral goat breeds. When domesticated their hair is collected by combing to remove the long fibre for spinning

Cashmere goat

The Angora Goat, as discussed previously, will provide fleece and meat but not milk, requiring it for its own offspring. It is a fibre goat that will provide two shearings a year with a yield of perhaps 6 to 8kg in total, perfect for hand spinners or small commercial batch spinning. The fleece blends extremely well with alpaca and certain sheep fleeces. This breed is covered in depth in Chapter 6.

Angora goats

RAISING GOATS

Cashgora is the name given to the angora crossbred goat. Sometimes they will have a coat which is worth harvesting by combing or shearing, but generally speaking they are a goat with hybrid vigour that will make a good meat goat.

Cashgora goats

MEAT SPECIFIC GOATS

The Boer Goat is the one meat specific goat in the UK. They are the Charolais cattle of the goat world. Always white with brown markings in the head region, they are strong, well built, kindly goats who will free range with good shelter all year round. They will grow to an adequate size for meat production earlier than a dairy goat or hybrid of the same. They are not milking goats and, like the Angora and Pygmy goat, need their milk for their offspring.

Boer goat

They are good goats to crossbreed with dairy or fibre varieties for meat carcasses. Do not keep these crosses for dairying as they are inefficient milkers and often produce kids with faults to their teats which makes them unusable as breeding animals in most cases.

CONSERVATION GOATS

There is really only one pure breed of goat that can be considered for conservation of wild terrain and this is the Bagot goat. Bagot goats are seriously in decline and are very much a goat for someone who has several acres of rough grazing where they can be as free as possible, so perhaps not the ideal smallholder goat, although the breed needs all the support it can get. They will still need the shelter of very good stone walls/ hedges and woodland and are not a breed you can simply turn out and forget about completely. They are also covered by all the regulations regarding domesticated goats.

Bagot goat

WHERE TO BUY?

Start in the classified advertisements of smallholder specific magazines. You can also contact the British Goat Society who will be able to tell you the breeders in your area and also the contacts for the various goat breed societies who could help you further. The British Goat Society website is www.allgoats.com. Be cautious about goats advertised in the local newspaper and take someone with you who knows about goats if you are tempted by such an advertisement.

RAISING GOATS

HOW MUCH SHOULD I PAY?

A quality dairy goat should cost around £200 but you will probably be able to find one for a little less.

Wethers (castrated males) are usually around £50.

Boer goats can be considerably more expensive than this and finding breeders with surplus stock can often be difficult, but if you are determined you should find some. The British Goat Society website should help you in your quest.

Angoras range from £100 to £200 depending on age, fleece and breeding.

Pygmy goats will cost around £75 to £150 each depending on age and breeding.

If it is simply companion goats you are after it maybe worth calling one of the animal rescue groups who often have animals for rehoming. You will not be allowed to breed from these goats though, so be quite sure what you want.

With good care a goat will live up to 16 years and be productive for most of those, but it must still be fed, so it is a bit like taking on a dog. Be absolutely sure that what you choose is what you really need. Find out as much information as you can from the breeder, get milking records, see vaccination and registration records and make sure the animals are correctly tagged. Do not make your mind up there and then. Go home and think about it and only then should you contact the seller the next day. Do not succumb to pressure to commit there and then. As a basic guide, if the goat looks sick or sorry, has a bad coat, missing teeth, running eyes or nose, a lumpy udder or is lame, walk away and find another. Ignore any excuses for poor health or appearance because any reputable goat keeper will only sell a good goat as she is the ambassador for the owner's entire herd.

ACCOMODATION AND FEEDING

BASIC FEEDING COSTS AND HUSBANDRY REQUIREMENTS

Week on week throughout the year a goat with access to reasonable grazing will cost around £4-£5 a week to keep depending on the area you live in (feed and bedding prices will determine this). In this figure I have factored in vaccination and routine worming, feed, hay and bedding. Pygmy or Bagot goats will cost less.

You should have a properly fenced enclosure or ideally half an acre for 2 goats plus a good draft proofed shed which is completely weather proof and affords the goats a minimum of 16 square feet each, and preferably more for the larger breeds.

There should be a clean water supply at all times and you should be available to tend the goats twice a day. You will also need a CPH Number BEFORE you move the goats to your home.(See Chapter 1). Introduce new goats to one another gradually and isolate new goats from other ruminants on the holding for ten days.Speak to your vet immediately if you think there any health problems in that period of time.

SHEDS AND SHELTERS

All goats need shelter from the elements both in summer and winter. They hate getting wet and, unlike sheep, their skin contains very little lanoline, so they quickly become saturated, cold and susceptible to infection as a result. A cold, wet goat will often become prone and quite literally give up and die. Similarly, during hot summer weather, they can suffer from sun burn and sunstroke. It is very difficult to reverse the effects of overheating in goats and death can follow very quickly. However, as long as goats have adequate shelter there is no reason why they cannot live outside all year round providing there is sufficient space so that their grazing areas stay well drained and do not become muddy.

Every goat needs a minimum of 16 square feet - in other words a space of no less than four feet by four feet. This is the minimum requirement and

RAISING GOATS

I normally allow 24 square feet for a dairy goat. This space can take the form of individual pens within a larger building such as a stable or barn. Pens can be created using sheep hurdles if all the individuals are on good terms or you can create a 'quiet' corner by wedging or attaching exterior ply to either the full length or part of the length of the pens.

There are purpose built goat sheds on the market which can be purchased for anything from £500 to £1000 depending on quality and the number of pens required. A garden shed will also suffice but it is worth lining out with sterling board as goats can often chew quite large holes in thin feather edge or tongue and groove timber. Wooden buildings should be treated with non-toxic wood preserver annually while the goats are away from the building for at least 48 hours. This ensures not only the life of the building but also that mites and fungal infections within the timber are killed.

Pole barn in construction

If your goats are to be free range, then a larger field shelter or a barn that has at least a third of the front covered works well. It is possible to build a pole barn of approximately 800 square feet (40 ´ x 20 ´) clad in profile sheeting and roofed with the same or a material such as Onduline for around £1500 and pole barns do not normally need planning permission unless you lay a concrete floor.This would accommodate around 30 goats in both winter and summer. The one pictured in construction did exactly that and was sited in five acres. The floor will need strawing and clearing out at least four times a year to avoid risks of infection and worms. If you do this clearing out with a tractor, don't leave the tractor in the field while you have a break. We did this and came back to find the hydraulics wrecked by several goats having chewed and severed tubes and cables! Goats do seem to have a sense of humour!

Completed pole barn

Pig arks can also provide good accommodation for free range goats providing they are large enough. You might need to modify them slightly so that you can shut the goats in on wild nights, but leave them sufficient ventilation. The beauty of a pig ark is that they can be moved by one person to face away from the wind if required. I find them extremely useful for rearing weaned kids as they can live as naturally as possible, but still have the benefit of shelter along with their freedom and the ability to interact and play with others of their own kind.

Free range Angora goats utilising a large pig ark

RAISING GOATS

The essentials of successful goat housing are:

❋ That the accommodation is draught free but well ventilated.
❋ That it is light and airy.
❋ That it is kept clean by regular mucking out and has thick dry bedding.
❋ That there is sufficient space to avoid bullying between goats.
❋ That goats with kids are given privacy and peace.

BEDDING MATERIALS

The cheapest bedding for goats is straw. They like straw and will usually pick it over and eat some of it when it is fresh. Once down for a few hours they will rarely continue to eat it. The downside, if you muck out every day or every few days, is that it can create a sizeable muck heap in a very short space of time. If you have plenty of land this is not going to be a problem, but it could be in a smaller space. All goat bedding will need topping up at a rate of two sections of straw per goat per day or slightly less in the case of free range goats with shelter.

Shavings and sawdust can also work very well. I have never known a goat eat this and an even better option is if you have rubber stable mats underneath. Rubber mats on their own with a scattering of absorbent bedding to soak up urine will also work well, but you will need to sweep it clean and disinfect it daily.

Miscanthus/hemp is becoming an increasingly popular bedding for all farm animals. It works well for goats, particularly on a soil floor, and can be deep littered on a soil floor without any bad odours. It composts quickly and well and as such can be very useful around your holding/garden.

Paper/cardboard is not a suitable bedding for goats.

FENCING

Secure fencing for your goats is an absolute necessity and it is worth spending some time and money on getting it right from the outset to save aggravation and grief later. If they escape they are likely to cause damage to crops and garden plants and will very likely poison themselves by eating toxic plants. If they escape onto your neighbours property or onto a road the legal implications may be costly. Much is going to depend on the area you have to fence and if you have a large acreage it is probably better to ring fence and then make smaller enclosures using electric fencing.

PERMANENT FENCING

If permanent fencing is your aim,then the best fencing available for goats is a high tensile graduated mesh fence such as Tornado, topped with a rail to which is attached a 12 or 18 inch outrigger. The outrigger should then carry an electric wire which is always switched on. Gates should be metal and mesh at the base (see picture P14). This fence was actually erected for multi-stock useage, so a fence which is dedicated to goats only need not have quite such a high specification but I still maintain the best goat stopper in the world is as close to this as you can get. It will provide you with years of maintenance and worry free goat keeping.

SEMI PERMANENT OR TEMPORARY FENCING

Cost is frequently an issue with permanent fencing and sometimes land is rented and, although it might be sheep or horse proof, it may well not be goat proof. It is also critical to keep the goats from eating toxic plants. I now live in Cornwall and this is a particular issue here as all the Cornish 'hedges'(which are really stone walls on which foliage grows to create a green stone wall) contain alkaloid plants which can kill goats. Out of necessity I have had to create a new type of semi-permanent fence for my goats which comprises 4" plastic electric fence posts threaded with five strands of electric wire at the base and topped with one strand of white electric tape. The whole thing is fired up with a solar powered electric fencing unit. It works extremely well, even keeping kids in, and because of the closeness of the strands I have not experienced any problems of horned goats getting themselves caught on the fencing. They have learned extreme respect for this fence! You can check that power is constant by attaching a fence detector which will flash if the electric charge is too low.

You will need to ensure that surrounding foliage is kept away from the fence lines by trimming it back once a week through the summer months and once a month during the winter with a strimmer or hand shears. Be careful not to catch the fence with the strimmer line as it will cut it. It might seem obvious but do remember to switch the fence off before you start!

Super solar powered electric goat fence

SHEEP NETTING

Electric sheep netting is not recommended for goats, either horned or otherwise. They easily get caught in it and kids especially can become entangled, receiving multiple shocks over a considerable period which is enough to kill them.

SHEEP HURDLES

Good quality, heavy duty sheep hurdles will create a temporary pen for goats within an enclosed area. They are particularly suitable for the early turn out of new born goats and kids. A pen like this can be several pens long/wide and give a sizeable area. Care should be taken that they can't collapse and tying the joints with twine can reduce this risk. Some kind of sheltered area should be created so that kids and mothers can be kept dry and out of direct sun. A water bucket attached to a bucket holder is also essential. Make sure that the narrowest bars of the hurdles are at the bottom of the pen so that kids cannot get their heads stuck and that it keeps dogs out. I use this method around a pig ark for the early turnout of does and kids.

The Golden Rules for all fencing are:

※   That they are secure and strong enough to endure the ministrations of the goat.
※   That it minimises risk of injury both to yourself and your stock and that it is suitable to prevent attack from predators.
※   That regular maintenance is carried out to keep it as good as the day it was erected.
※   That electric tapes and wires are kept free of vegetation.
※   That mains operated electric fences are switched off during thunder storms.

BREEDING FROM YOUR CHOSEN GOATS

NANNIES AND BILLIES: CHOOSING THE RIGHT BUCK

Generally speaking goats cycle between July and March in the UK, although there are regional variations on this depending on the temperature, but oestrus is mainly geared to starting at the time of the year when the days are longest.

RAISING GOATS

TIMING

The timing of your decision to mate your goat will depend on what your intention is for kidding and general management of the kids, milking the doe and so on. The gestation period of a goat is 5 months (between 151 and 154 days) so you will need to work back from the date which you would ideally like the kids to be born. This will depend on your working week, the destiny of the kids and how much time you have to milk the goat(s) for your household supply. If your goats are stall-fed all or some of the time, then the timing in terms of weather conditions is less critical than if your goats are living outside. All goats should have access to shelter but kidding outside is fine providing the nights are warm enough. By this I mean the difference in temperature between noon and midnight. Early in the year it can be wet and mild and the temperature between noon and midnight perhaps only changes by 10°C. Later in the year night time temperatures have, on occasions in the South of England, fallen to 4°C when it has been 24°C during the day. This is too big a temperature shock to a new born kid and is why I suggest you address the intended kidding time carefully, especially if you intend to kid outdoors.

In the regions of the world where goats originated the timing of the kidding is irrelevant because temperatures are generally higher than in the UK, even though they can be very low overnight. Because goats will naturally seek cave type shelter overnight and in large groups the safety (and temperature safety) of the new born kids is taken care of.

SIGNS AND SYMPTOMS OF OESTRUS

The goat will invariably bleat a lot. Some breeds, especially the Anglo-Nubian, can be particularly noisy at this time! Their sole aim is, of course, to attract a mate which in the wild it would manage extremely successfully and very likely be mated several times by several different bucks. This is what nature intended. However, in the domesticated goats in our charge this process is not given free reign unless you have a few of last year's uncastrated males running about! The doe will flick and wag her tail, often carrying it in a'hooky'stance and there may be some clear discharge and reddening and slight swelling of the vulva. Some goats are not particularly demonstrative when in season and so you should keep a daily eye on the back end if you are hoping to breed from them.

Goats cycle every 18 days for about 48 to 72 hours. Ideally they should be mated 2 or 3 times during that period to be absolutely sure of a successful conception. Generally speaking I have found that a healthy doe will often be in kid after only one mating. If she is not ready for mating she will not stand for the buck and absolutely no persuasion should be attempted. If the goat does not return in season in the next 21 days you can be pretty confident that you have been successful!

HOW TO CHOOSE YOUR BUCK

Before choosing your buck you must ask yourself only one question: what do I want the kids for?

The possibilities are:

❋ Just so that I have my doe in milk for household use
❋ So that I have kids to sell
❋ Meat
❋ Growing the herd
❋ Showing
❋ All or some of these

If your main purpose is to keep your goat milking it doesn't really matter what the origins of the buck are and it could indeed be a kid over 16 weeks of age or a young buckling of your own from the previous year from a different goat. Remember that male kids are sexually active from 16 weeks of age (sometimes earlier!), and for that matter so are young does, but mating a doe as young as four months is not recommended as she is still a kid herself, will not be fully grown, may have a difficult or hopeless kidding and will almost certainly not reach her own growth potential. Male kids become bucklings from January. Therefore a male kid born in August, although in theory only a kid the following spring, falls in to the category of buckling on January 1st, even though he is only five months old.

So it is quite alright to use a young male. He may be destined for a trip down the road later and end up in the you know what afterwards, but at least he 'lived' in the fullest sense of the word. Certainly if your nearest stud buck is a long way off, this solves a perennial problem. You can let him run with the female/s in question, but he should not be expected to serve more than 3 animals in his first year. All you will have to do is keep an eye on things and make a note in your diary or wall planner of when you think the mating took place. The buckling will make it very plain when he is interested in her and there will be no doubt that she is coming into season! The fact that he might be half the size of the doe is also irrelevant. Goats are natural born gymnasts!

If you have a nice pure bred and registered goat which you are or might like to show, it stands to reason that you should, if at all possible, use a registered buck of the same breed. This way you will have kids to sell if that is your requirement. Male kids may present you with a problem, but it is worth mentioning them within your breed society before you castrate them in case someone is looking for a potential stud goat or a buckling that can be used in the way I previously described. Female kids will either expand your herd or be saleable to others with an interest in that breed. Finding a buck through the breed society should be fairly straightforward and you always have the option of artificial insemination (AI) if the distance to travel is too far. The breed society should be able to advise you of goat keepers in the area who operate an AI service. My personal experience of AI for goats has been somewhat disappointing, but I may have been unlucky.

If you want kids for meat (and you don't have to feel that you can't use female kids for meat either), then choose a meat breed stud male such as a Boer or Boer cross. Failing that an Anglo-Nubian should produce hybrid vigour in the kids as will a British Saanen (generally larger than the Saanen). An Angora buck will also put a very good meaty carcase on a goat, though it will not be so large. Actually any kids will grow on well for meat, but I'm trying to maximise the potential for you.
Assuming that you are not going to use one of your own homebred males then check a number of things with the owner of the stud buck.

※ Fertility rates
※ See some of his progenyy if possible
※ Has he been CAE tested: this is best practice but not essential (see

Chapter 7 for an explanation of this)

✳ Is he MV tested: again best practice but not essential (see Chapter 7 for an explanation of this)

✳ Is he regularly wormed and vaccinated (this will be a foregone conclusion with a professional breeder but nobody is going to laugh at you for asking these questions, quite the contrary)

✳ If you are wanting to grow your herd to good vigorous milkers, ask about the milk yields of his close relatives, particularly his dam and sire's dam.

Most professional breeders will ask you to 'walk in' your goat on the day/days she is in season for mating. Some will take the goat for a few days or longer. Sometimes you may find someone who is prepared to bring their goat to you.

.....AND IN THE END

The main thing to decide is WHY you want to breed from your goat and what the consequences of this will be. How will you cope with any unwanted male kids and are you prepared to rear them yourself for meat and see the process through or castrate them and keep them long term as pets or companions?

Please don't breed from your goat for the 'aah' factor of kids without an action plan. As previously stated, young male kids are sexually active from 16 weeks onwards and will mate their own mother if allowed to and move into the stage in life where, if they were humans, they would be arrested most Friday nights! The law of averages says that you are likely to get at least one male kid with every kidding from every goat. So decide on your action plan before you mate your doe. Write it all down and stick to it!

CHAPTER 3

FEEDING YOUR GOATS ECONOMICALLY THROUGHOUT THE YEAR

AUTUMN AND WINTER

As far as your goats are concerned, feeding the best diet you can will ensure good growth and a prolific milk supply throughout the best and worst months of the year.

HAY- HAYLAGE - STRAW

First decide the winter regime you will put your goats on. Will it be hay, a hay/straw mix or haylage?

Whatever you decide you should stick to it and not make changes as these will effect the goats' productivity and health.

My own choice has always been to buy the very best I can and to this end I buy either Farm Assured Haylage (this is VERY important - you need the haylage to be properly tested and see the certificate to make sure there are no foreign micro-organisms and also the protein levels. Cheap haylage is almost certainly going to give you a problem) or a branded product such as Horsehage. Although expensive, a bale of Horsehage will last one goat for a week if supported by concentrates and some grazing or browsings. You can 'pad' this out if necessary by feeding good barley straw alongside. If you can find good quality meadow hay or rye grass hay this too is excellent too but it MUST be free from mould and smell sweet. This is something that becomes increasingly difficult during bad years with a poor harvest. First crop top quality hay will always be sold at a premium.

Always buy HORSE quality hay for goats!

CONCENTRATES

The most economical and well balanced form of concentrates is a mix which is branded and will contain all the nutrients and vitamins needed. You can mix your own concentrates if you wish, but this is only viable if you have 6 or more goats. You should always make sure that it has a good mix of maize, oats, barley, alfalfa and linseed cake and should also supplement it with a goat specific supplement such as Caprivite. Feed branded concentrates according to the instructions on the package and home made mixes at a rate of 1kg per day to milkers in a minimum of 2 feeds and a teacupful of soaked sugar beet pulp can also be added to each feed if it is liked by the goats. Also add any dried herbs or nettles that you may have prepared earlier in the year on a daily basis. Stale bread which has been oven baked and broken up plus any vegetable trimmings (though not potato), apples, ageing bananas etc. from your household will all be readily eaten.

NB. This does not count as the taboo 'catering waste' as long as it has not been in contact with any animal products such as meat or milk products including cheese, butter and eggs.

A goat specific salt and mineral block is a good idea and a very large one tied up with a rope will keep several goats going for a whole winter. I like the larger blocks because several goats can lick at any one time which makes it a bit of a social event for them!

A social mineral block 'licked from all sides!'

RAISING GOATS

THE VIABILITY OF OVER WINTERING ALL OF YOUR STOCK

This is a touchy subject as many goats are kept as pets BUT now is the time to seriously consider the ongoing cost of your goats. If you think it will be difficult to feed them all effectively it might be wise to consider which ones you might sell or cull.

Your meat goats are worth spending a little more on to produce an earlier carcase and you should perhaps weigh up the advantages/disadvantages of a smaller carcase and an earlier kill.

Your dairy goats cannot be skimped on if you want them to stay productive and/or produce healthy kids in the spring. Work out your finances, if they are a consideration in you enterprise and stick to your decisions regarding sales, culling and breeding.

The cost of keeping all livestock will always increase. Your stock value should also increase, but it will only do so if your herd is healthy and well fed. This influences carcase value and 'on the hoof' value too.

SPRING AND SUMMER

Depending on your circumstances, spring and summer offer the easiest time for managing your goats with regard to feeding. If you have grazing or scrub and grazing let the sward grow until it is around 2 inches long before turning your goats out for the spring. This is the optimum length for grazing. Once the sward gets lower than that you will have to supplement your goats grazing in a number of ways. For further information on rearing goats for meat please go to Chapter 5.

SUPPLEMENTARY FEEDING IN SPRING AND SUMMER

Supplementary feeding can consist of concentrated feeds such as a proprietory goat mix, alphalfa, soaked, molassed or unmollassed sugar beet pulp and/or hay/ haylage or straw. Some commercial herds use other bulk purchased feeds but, for the purposes of domestic goat keeping, I am sticking to the staple feeds.

If your goats have been housed or partially housed during the winter months you can cut back their concentrate ration by half when you initially turn them out for the spring and summer. Continue to feed some hay until the goats cease to be interested in it. If the weather is wet the goats are likely to stay under cover, in which case make sure they have enough fibre in the form of hay, straw or haylage. Continue to give them access to a caprine specific mineral/salt lick.

Does with kids at foot have high nutritional needs, especially if they are providing milk for the house as well, and will need to be brought away from goats without kids to be fed twice daily with a specific amount of concentrates (see Chapter 7 - Kidding and Post Kidding).

Don't overstock your space. Half an acre should support four goats throughout the year with supplementary feeding from the end of July through to April the following year. This can be variable but generally speaking in the UK, the proteins and sugars drop in grass and other herbage from the end of July and do not rise significantly again until the following spring. In October there is often a flush of growth and so this needs to be monitored.

LONG FIBRE

Long fibre is an important part of any goat's diet and so, if your grass is too short, your goats will aim for longer stemmed wild plants and the bark on trees, occasionally ingesting food which is poisonous to them. It is therefore vital to ensure that long fibre is available to them in one form or another. If the land does not offer this option then continue to leave hay for them in a dry location where it cannot be trampled on. A wheeled sheep feeder is perfect for this. A whole bale or a mix of straw and hay can be put into this and the goats will take it as required. Do not put haylage in these feeders unless you are sure it will be consumed within 3 days. Haylage goes mouldy after this time and will not be eaten, giving the incorrect impression that the goats are not hungry. If your grass and general herbage is long be careful that your goats don't gorge this initially and become bloated (see chapter 7 - Bloat). If this is the case restrict the

RAISING GOATS

time spent on the verdant areas until it has started to become grazed down.

Suitable sheep feeder

Another way to supplement your goat's long fibre is to collect it yourself. Going out with a pair of secateurs and cutting branches and other forage from the hedgerows works well. Try not to make an obvious 'hole' in the natural growth, cutting as you would to harvest garden vegetables. That way you can go back for more later on without damaging the hedgerow. Your garden might also provide various options throughout the year. Prunings and clearings from pea crops, for instance, are often greatly appreciated. Always be mindful of poisonous plants such as the aerial parts of tomatoes and potatoes, rhubarb and raw beans (see Chapter 7 -Plants Poisonous to all Ruminants by Ingestion).

WATER

All goats need a permanent supply of clean drinking water.

IN THE FIELD

If your goats are free range and there is a stream in the field, this could be a useful source, providing the goats can reach it without having to enter the water or descend a steep bank. Goats such as Angoras can get quickly saturated by river and stream water and their long coats can become so heavy that they are unable to get out and eventually get chilled, collapse and drown. There is also a possible risk of contamination upstream by dead livestock or animals, particularly in upland regions of the country. If possible free range goats should have a water trough which is emptied and cleaned every week. Failing that, buckets or a suitable receptacle which is not too deep should be filled at least daily from a clean water source. The depth is important. An old bath or water tank is not suitable for smaller goats or kids as they can jump in, get trapped and drown. I usually put a small sulphur block into my outside water containers. These can be obtained at most pet shops for use in dogs' water bowls and have the effect of cleansing the water should it become contaminated during the day with bird droppings in particular. This, however, does not supersede the need to scrub out the trough or container on a weekly basis! Goats, despite their reputation for 'eating everything' actually don't and they detest dirty food and water and would rather starve or die of dehydration than eat or drink either.

IN A STALL

Water in a stall should ideally be in a bucket holder and placed at head height for the smallest goat. It should be changed twice daily. Some keepers add a teaspoon of salt to their goats' drinking water to ensure they have an adequate supply but my own choice is a mineral/salt block within the stall or field as previously described. There is a drowning risk to new born kids or kids at kidding with water buckets in stalls and they should be removed for the actual kidding of a goat as the doe in her labouring may stand to kid and drop the kid into the bucket. At this time, if there is any chance of the doe kidding while you are not there, make sure that the bucket is held at a height that is outside of her kidding height range. In the first few days after birth the bucket should be at the does reachable head height but not low enough for an adventurous kid to fall into.

WARM OR COLD?

A newly delivered goat or a sick one will often drink warm water where it might not drink cold and that is always worth remembering.

Raising Goats

Harvesting Summer Herbs for Your Goats

Goats are browsers, not grazers, and appreciate a wide range of plants and herbs throughout the summer which may not be available during the winter months. This can vary from region to region over the country. Where I live, in Cornwall, we are lucky to have a mild climate and seldom experience frost and snow. As a result, many summer plants grow well even during the shortest days of the year and so hand harvesting of the goat's favourite plants is fairly easy for 12 months of the year. Previously I lived in East Anglia where winters are colder and frost and snow can persist for several weeks. Here it was important to harvest some of the more essential herbage for winter use. Good hay is essential and we can always supplement the diet artificially with feed additives and supplements such as Caprivite which is specially prepared for goats, but there is great satisfaction to be had in doing it yourself for free in the certain knowledge that this is the way it was meant to be. In their natural habitats goats hail from the warmer climates of the world where herbage grows all the time. To some extent we can imitate this by DIY harvesting of summer plants and herbs. If you are unsure of identifying the various plants get a book from the library or research them on the internet. If you are lucky enough to have rough grazing for your goats, watch them and see which plants they prefer.

NETTLES(Urtica dioica)

Years ago it was widely accepted that the feeding of nettles improved milk yield. Goats will often eat young nettles while they are still growing, but prefer wilted ones. Harvesting nettle throughout the summer when it is most prolific is a very useful food source for goats in the winter months. Strim or shear them down on a warm day late in the morning when the dew has gone and allow them to lay on the land for a couple of hours before collecting and hanging them to dry over a fence (where the goats are not present!) or on a wooden pallet or something similar. Turn them every time you pass and, in a few hours on a hot day or a few days when it is less warm, they should be dry enough to stuff in to paper sacks (not plastic) for winter storage. Feed a handful to each goat daily. If you start to harvest nettles from your fields early in the season before they flower, you should get several croppings from the same clump. Nettles are an excellent source of Vitamin C, calcium and iron.

DEAD NETTLE(Lamium album)

This is worth harvesting and drying as it is an excellent cure for scour. Half a cupful of the dried plant is my first attack on scour when it is only effecting one animal. Interestingly, it works equally effectively on a constipated animal! If more than one is affected with scour then you should suspect a worm burden such as coccidiosis. Harvest at the point of flowering.

THISTLE (Circium vulgare)

Wilted thistles are eagerly eaten by goats. They are also enjoyed when dried for winter use. Harvest them before they go to seed (no fluffy bits!) and this will also help to keep your pasture free from the proliferation of thistle when they seed each year. Felling them at the point they go to seed is counter productive and spreads the seed over a wide area. Dry them as with nettles and store them in the same way.

CLEAVERS (Galium aperine)

Cleavers are also known as goose grass, sweet heart and sticky willy and are very good for cleansing of the lymphatic system and maintaining skin condition. Geese also love them. They are easy to pull up in great quantities. Dry them as before and feed them in the same manner.

MEADOWSWEET (Filipendula ulmaria)

This grows wild in many places, especially wetlands, and can be easily cultivated in the garden. The flower heads have a distinctive honey smell, but it is the leaves that we need to harvest before flowering takes place. Avoid harvesting when flowering as the plant needs to propagate. Cut the stems close to the ground and tie them in bundles to dry in a building or in the sunshine depending on the weather. Once dry, store them in open paper sacks. The leaves will fall to the bottom of the bag and can be crushed and fed with the course ration. The twigs are greatly enjoyed tied high in the stall for the goats to chew. Apart from being a real treat for your goats it also contains salicylic acid (aspirin) and so is particularly good for the older or arthritic goat.

WILD GARLIC (Allium ursinula)

This plant grows in more acidic soils and the leaves should be harvested in April, May or June in cooler parts of the country. Pick them before flowering and dry flat on chicken wire or weld mesh sheets. As drying utensils these will come in handy again later on when we talk about shearing Angora Goats, but will also be a perennial Godsend if you intend to harvest and dry herbage every year). The leaves may take up to a week to dry and when they are fully dried they should be crushed and stored in an airtight container for mixing in the course ration in the same way as the meadowsweet leaves. Wild garlic is good for the respiratory system, aids digestion and gut flora and also creates a hostile environment for helminths (worms) - it is also pretty nice for seasoning your food too as it is milder than a garlic bulb.

HIPS, BERRIES & FRUITS

Rosehips and hawthorn berries are also worth drying for winter use. They are both part of the rose family. They make excellent titbits for your goats and are nutritious too, being high in Vitamin C and also good for digestion. Pick and dry them indoors near a moderate heat source. If you have an Aga then the bottom oven for a few days is perfect. Store them in an airtight container once dried completely. (Dried citrus fruit peel is also enjoyed by some goats and can be dried very well in an Aga using the same method.)A warm airing cupboard will also do the trick, but remember to shake them about every so often or they may develop mildew. If this happens at any time, discard the berries or hips as the moulds forming could be damaging to your animals. Just a few every now and again make a special natural treat.

If you are lucky enough to have a small drying machine, and I know some smallholders do have these, then the sky is the limit on drying berries for animals and this can also extend to fruit such as apples. Cored and cut into rings they will again make a welcome treat for your goat. At the point of harvest the cores can be fed back to the goats as part of their daily ration. I would suggest no more than 20 a day per animal though to avoid gut imbalance. Remember to give your goat everything in moderation and make no sudden dietary changes regardless of how much of a glut you may have.

If you are harvesting in the countryside, make sure you only take a small percentage of the plants listed as they are valuable habitats for many species and should not be harvested in such a way that it looks like you have been there. On the other hand , if you take these plants from alongside footpaths you will be doing walkers a great service, particularly with regard to nettles!

All of these harvested and dried plants are best stored in paper sacks in the same kind of environment that you would store your best hay. If they are mouldy they have not been stored well enough or perhaps not been dried sufficiently. If this is the case, do not feed them but add them to your compost/muck heap where they will do far more good than to your goat in this state.

DOMESTICATE AND COMPENSATE

GENERAL MAINTENANCE AND CARE OF YOUR GOATS

Other than being well fed and watered , there are regular jobs that must be done for your goats and other jobs which are nice to do both for you and your goats but not essential.

HOOF TRIMMING

Hoof trimming needs to be done every six to eight weeks, eight weeks being the absolute maximum. Goats' feet are easy to trim if attended to regularly and regular handling of the feet from a kid onwards will make it an easy and rewarding task.

RAISING GOATS

The goat has a cloven hoof: in other words it comprises of two claws on every foot. In the natural state these claws wear down easily on a natural terrain of rocky outcrops and desert sand where many of our goat breeds originated. In the domesticated state this does not happen and so, like all animals that we domesticate, we have to compensate for the losses gained by not living in a natural habitat. The goat, being a flight animal, does need to have the ability to move and a goat with over long feet or problems associated with that state will be lame, sometimes very lame. Once lame it can be a long process to correct as weight bearing on the offending hoof is affected, causing stresses and strains on a corresponding hoof so it can be a long and ongoing situation. All this can be avoided by correct and regular trimming.

EQUIPMENT NEEDED

Hoof shears
An old scrubbing brush or dandy brush
A hoof knife, if preferred
A surfoam rasp or similar
Coarse sandpaper
Hoof oil or olive oil

METHOD

First, with your goat wearing a collar or goat style head collar, tie her up to a suitable tie ring or get someone to hold her for you.

Next, standing at her left (near side) shoulder and facing the tail, run your hand down her foreleg to the fetlock joint and gently but firmly lift her foot. She may well pick it up for you. Bring the foot between your knees and grip it, but not too tightly with your knees. This give you 2 hands with which to work on the foot.

With the hoof shears cut right round the outside edge of the foot so that it is almost level with the sole. You may need to brush the foot off first to clean it of any debris.

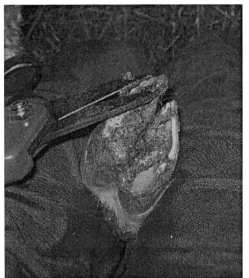
Holding the hoof for trimming

Cut the heel level to the sole. If this is your first time trimming a foot, take a little at a time so that you don't cut too deep and cause the foot to bleed. If you do cut too deep and the foot bleeds, don't panic! Spray it with purple spray (see Chapter 7 - First Aid Kit). This is not an ideal situation and the goat will be lame for a few days, so try to limit this by taking your time. After you have trimmed a few hooves you will have got the hang of it!

Once you have trimmed with the shears, run the surefoam rasp across and around the hoof and check that it is level on both sides. Finish off with a rub with course sandpaper.

Finally, give the inside and outside and between the claws a good rub with hoof oil. This is the sort you use for horses. The oil will finish the job nicely and will also help to keep the horn in good condition and assist in the avoidance of fungal infection.

Then move on to the near hind foot, then the off hind foot and finally the off fore. If you use the same sequence every time the goat will soon learn the routine and be very biddable.

GROOMING

Although it is not absolutely essential to groom a goat, they do enjoy it and, if you have the time, so will you. If you intend to show your goats in the summer then daily grooming for a few weeks before the shows start will show in the condition of your goat's coat.

When goats moult they tend to rub their coats on whatever is available

RAISING GOATS

to rid themselves of itchy excess hair and so, at this time of year, a really good groom with a rubber curry comb every few days will really help and could well save your fences!

Certain breeds such as the Cashmere need combing in order to harvest the coat, but that is dealt with in Fibre Goats (see Chapter 6).
Angora goats need twice yearly shearing if you are to collect their fibre. This is dealt with in depth in Chapter 6.

BATHING

Goats do not need regular bathing, but if they are to be shown some goat keepers will bath them beforehand. Personally I prefer grooming. Grooming will bring about a lustre to the coat that no amount of bathing can do. However, some of the white breeds such as Saanens and Boers may well benefit from a bath before a show.

If a goat has suffered from dietary scour its back end may be quite messy and this definitely needs washing off or it can attract blow flies and create soreness for the goat.

Tie your goat up and wash with warm water and shampoo. Rinse and dry it, then smear the area with some petroleum jelly if the scour is ongoing to protect the skin (see Chapter 7- Dietary Scour).

After kidding the goat will suffer a bloody discharge for some days and again will benefit from the same treatment as above. Sometimes it becomes necessary to trim long tail hairs with scissors at this time. The back of the udder can also become dirty and this also needs cleaning, especially if you are milking for human use.

WORMING

WHY DO WE NEED TO WORM?

Parasitic challenge to goats is both huge and varied. In fact, when you read most Veterinary books on the subject you are inclined to wonder how goats survive at all! If we don't deal with endoparasites we will have an unthrifty animal which, after a short or sometimes quite a long time will die, probably from repeated bouts of diarrhoea and very likely in agony. She will pass her parasitic infection on to her kids which will also become unthrifty and die in the same way but sooner. This may sound rather dramatic but at the very least we will end up with a sad, thin, goat with a bad staring coat, a lack of appetite and repeated digestive problems. They will infect their pasture and anything else following them will suffer the same fate.

In the wild state goats cover more ground and the parasitic challenges are less, but in reality they probably live much shorter lives. Today, as with human life, we expect our domestic animals to live to a ripe old age and they usually do as long as the care we give them is adequate and we protect them from the diseases and infections that we inflict upon them by domestication. We love them and we care and so their health is of vital importance to us.

THE ORGANIC OPTION

For many the very concept of keeping a goat or two for household use encompasses the desire to move away from the chemically adulterated world we live in and is perceived to be a safe way to drink unpasteurised milk and its related products.

When I ran a commercial herd trying to achieve an 'organic state' was my main goal and as a result I used flowers of sulphur (sulphur sublimed) in their diet as an ongoing preventative for coccidiosis and found to my surprise that within a month of using it I had not only a coccidiosis free herd but a herd that repeatedly returned close to negative worm counts. Personally, I now never use commercial wormers and continue to use flowers of sulphur on my 'house goats' now I have domestic goats again.

There are now organic wormers on the market, Vermex being just one of them, which work by giving prophylactic doses and regular worm counts. The company can be found online and the product is available through most smallholder retail outlets.

RAISING GOATS

THE COMMERCIAL OPTIONS

I choose my words carefully here when I say 'commercial' rather than 'chemical' – I know if I say chemical someone will inevitably say "But Sulphur is a chemical."Well, yes, it is, but it is NATURALLY occurring and that is the difference.

First of all let us look at the various endoparasitic challenges available to your goats:

ROUNDWORMS – varying from 5–30mm in length, some of these are visible to the naked eye, however, lack of visibility does not necessarily mean that your goat is free from them. There are a variety of different worms that fall into this category and to describe them all and their actions in this article would take up an entire chapter, and so I will attempt to gather them under one umbrella. The danger zones for goats are at the end of May and early June and then again in August and September - this is as a result of the following batch of larvae from the May/June ones! Mid-April to mid-May are also danger zones' for nematodirus infestation which also falls into the Roundworm category. So already we see that mid-April right through to September - most of the spring and summer, in fact – present huge challenges from this family of worms. The best strategy is to dose your females immediately after kidding (the second or third day) which will be before you are taking milk for yourself or anyone else. That way the kids will get some residue as well. You must be guided by the manufacturer's instructions with regard to human milk withdrawal times, depending on which preparation you choose - and this should be discussed with your vet if possible).

LUNGWORM - can infect goats and is manifested by coughing as the worms live in the airways of the animal. Untreated, lungworm can lead to a type of pneumonia known as parasitic pneumonia. Its lifecycle is quite similar to that of the Roundworm, but it has an additional cycle where the adult larvae migrate to the lungs via the bloodstream. The goat coughs up the eggs and then swallows them, allowing them to return to the gut and be excreted in the droppings where they are picked up again by the next passing goat. This phase tends to happen again in early summer and so the choice of wormer (anthalmintic) should encompass both species.

Again. your vet will advise but it will be a Fenbendazole,Oxfendazole or Albendazole based wormer.

All of these latter 3 medicines will also deal with⋯

TAPEWORM - From all the studies I have read there seems to be little material available on this parasite in goats, so perhaps it isn't such a problem.

FLUKE - Fluke or 'Liver Fluke' is a parasite which can affect all ruminants and makes its home in the liver - the bile ducts to be precise. The mud snail is the host for this problem and in theory the problem will be worse in wet, low lying areas where drainage is poor. There are 2 different species. Again it is an affliction of warmer weather. The eggs need an outside temperature of 10°C or above to hatch and the land needs to be wet. This sounds like a typical early summer or autumn in Britain to me – so there you are - the challenge is there again! Albendazole is, as far as I know, the only drug that will deal with this one.

WHAT ELSE CAN WE DO?

1.Keep stocking rates down. Be realistic about how many goats you can keep on the area of land you have available. I usually work on no more than five dairy sized goats or nine Angoras to an acre. If you have Pygmies you can probably get away with 12. Dose the females and other adults and goatlings all together straight after kidding and then every four to six weeks from May to September. DO NOT DOSE KIDS LESS THAN 6 WEEKS OLD! If you have the space move the goats to clean pasture after your June administration ie. pasture that has had other stock on it. If the goats come in for the winter, dose all of them together as they come in.

2.Decide on a worming regime for your goats. Discuss it with your vet so that you don't waste money on the wrong anthalmintic or over or underdose your animals.

3.Don't think that because your goats are stall fed that they will not be challenged by worms. They may well be free from worms but they can also be far more easily challenged by them because they have built up

RAISING GOATS

no resistance. Taking them to shows poses a risk, as does feeding them grass or herbage from places where other goats have grazed. It is wise therefore to have a worming regime, although it may not need to be as vigorous as for the grazed goat.

4.Do not turn your kids out onto the same pasture every year. Fence your paddock in half if you need to and put them in alternate halves each year! The risk of the Roundworm Nematodiriasis is an enormous challenge. Alternatively, keep your kids indoors until the end of May when the risk from Nematodes has effectively passed.

As a rule all goats should be wormed regularly.

PARASITE CONTROL

Occasionally goats may become infested with lice or forage mites (see Chapter 7). Routine ectoparasites control is a good habit to get into. Every spring and autumn (typically at the change of coat) dress your goat from poll to tail with a proprietory louse powder. Care should be taken to avoid contact with the eyes. Both organic and chemical based powders and sprays can be obtained from most smallholder retail outlets and agricultural merchants. Spot On for sheep is a good one but is not licensed for use in goats, which unfortunately is the same for many preparations. The only rule to observe from the perspective of a milking goat is that if the milk is being consumed by humans, is this the right preparation for you. Similarly, if the fleece of an Angora or the hair of a Cashmere is being harvested, it will not be acceptable for use in organic production unless an appropriate organic treatment has been used.

VACCINATION

Routine vaccination is not a legal requirement for goats, but it is a wise precaution.

CHAPTER 4

KEEPING DAIRY GOATS

Once you have chosen your breed of dairy goat and sourced and bought them you are on your way. If it is solely dairying you have in mind then you will probably have 2 milking goats or a milking goat with a goatling daughter or companion wethered son. She may be in milk already or be awaiting the birth of kids. Whichever permutation you have decided on, the cardinal issue is how to go about milking and maintaining that animal.

Most dairy goats will be stalled in part. They might be outside during the day with access to shelter and stalled within a building at night. Her diet will depend on the time of year and her stage in life.

As a general rule weaned kids and goatlings need a high fibre diet which will consist mainly of the best hay/haylage you can find, plus grass and general browsings from their paddock or forage that you have collected for them including branches and leaves. Concentrates can also be fed if required and these should consist of a proprietory goat mix fed according to instructions as they all vary depending on the protein content of the feed. This can also be supplemented with soaked sugar beet (but no more than 2 cupfuls of soaked beet per day per animal) and perhaps Alpha A, although this is not an ideal goat feed as it is too short and is also very expensive. With a proprietory branded goat mix no additional vitamin supplements should be needed.

The most important thing to remember is that it is virtually impossible to overfeed a goat with fibre but it is very easy to overfeed a goat with concentrates. The latter can result in serious gut disturbance and even death, so only ever feed according to instructions and keep the feed bag secure in a lidded bin to avoid accidental feed theft by your goats!

RAISING GOATS

ADJUSTING NEW GOATS TO ONE ANOTHER

If you have purchased goats from more than one source, be prepared to give them time to become accustomed to one another. They need to be able to see but not touch initially. Once they have been housed side by side for about a week, you should have no problems with them getting along with one another. It is important to give them this time, especially as they might be in kid or have full udders. Fighting does occur and they can be extremely aggressive to one another and bite ears and udders as well as butting each other both on the head and flanks. Much damage can be done and so this early introduction is all important. Once 2 does have taken a dislike to one another it is often almost impossible to stem the resulting aggression and this creates a management nightmare both at this point and, even worse, when later on they will have kids at foot.

Avoid buying horned and hornless (either disbudded or polled) dairy goats together. The horned goat will always be at an advantage over the hornless one and bullying can ensue. If you mix dairy goats with other breeds such as Angoras or horned Pygmies this will not be a problem as the dairy goat will be superior in size.

MILKING YOUR GOAT

METHOD AND TECHNIQUE

MILKING FROM SCRATCH

Having acquired your dairy goat either as a purchase or by breeding, the object of the exercise now is to provide hygienically produced dairy products for your house on as long a term basis as possible.

If you have bought in the doe as a dairy goat and she has no kids at foot, you now have a twice daily routine to maintain with no days off! You, or someone who is known to the goat, must be prepared to milk as far as possible every twelve hours in order to maintain a constant milk supply without health hazard to either yourself or the goat. Think VERY carefully about this before you buy and commit to this undertaking.

Alternatively, (in my own opinion, essentially) you will either have bred from this doe yourself or bought her with one or two kids at foot who are suckling from her. Even if the kids are three months old, as long as they have had free access to the udder from birth you will have no problem in converting this animal to a useful dairy provider.

My own preference in the management of 'house' dairy goats is not to wean the kids at an early age. I leave the kids on the mother for 2 weeks full time. When the kids are beginning to eat some concentrate ration and hay or grass, which will be at around this age, I separate the doe from the kids for 12 hours overnight. I then milk the doe first thing in the morning and then return the kids to mum for the rest of the day. This works well if you are out at work during the day for obvious reasons, but can also work well if you have many jobs to do on the holding during the day or have young children to consider. The added benefit is that the kids will 'strip out' the mother's udder thoroughly after you have milked and this will lower the risks of mastitis tremendously. When you separate the kids from the doe, put them in an adjacent pen where they can see the mother and she them but make sure that the sides are high enough that neither of the parties will take a leap into the other pen. I once had a very agile Golden Guernsey who could do this and further demonstrated her advanced intelligence by jumping back into her pen when she heard me approach in the morning! It took me several days of spying to fully comprehend the scenario that day after day had resulted in an empty udder after 12 hours in isolation!

The kids need to be fed a small amount of concentrate/creep feed at the point of separation and some fresh browsings or hay to keep them going overnight. Also make sure that they have a clean water supply which is in a shallow bucket into which they can easily reach. If you have a number of free range does, the best way is to bring the kids up to a building overnight for their own safety. You can put similarly aged kids in a building together and they will have tremendous fun playing. Give them some old cardboard boxes and perhaps a bale of straw in the middle of the pen to jump on. In the morning they always find the right mother, so you can usually just let them out and open the gate to the mothers' field. If you are milking more than one goat, don't let the kids back to the mothers until you have milked them all. It can get very noisy otherwise!

MILKING TECHNIQUE

First bring your goat into a quiet enclosed area which is clean and free of soiled bedding, free range hens or anything else that can contaminate the milk. Keep your dogs/cats/chickens out of the milking area while you are milking. (This is essential if you are going to milk commercially and this will be explained later in this chapter).

If you are lucky enough to have a milking bench so much the better, and the goat will quickly learn to jump up on it as soon as you put some food in a bucket at the front of the stand. I find it is just as easy to stand the goat on the normal floor surface and sit on a low stool or one of those plastic footstools that you can buy in most hardware stores for a few pounds. Make a small pen with some hurdles or have the goat stand close to a solid wall so that she has a 'stop' to one side of her.

You will need the following:

⁎ A bucket of warm water with a non-tainting sterilising fluid added to it.
⁎ 4 dry clean cloths (such as a standard dish cloth) for each goat you are going to milk OR proprietary udder wipes
⁎ Udder Cream
⁎ A clean receptacle for milking into, with a lid. Stainless steel is best but a small plastic bucket kept solely for the purpose will do equally well.
⁎ A small plastic cup

The most important thing with milking is to avoid contamination, so you must make every effort to achieve this, particularly if you do not want to pasteurise the milk which will inevitably change its qualities.
Wear clean clothes or better still an overall kept solely for the purpose and stored in a plastic bag between milkings.

If you are right handed you will probably feel most comfortable milking on the goat's near (left) side. If you are left handed then the opposite will apply

Bring the goat to the milking area and attach her to a tie ring or to the bars of the pen. She must be comfortable but not have enough rope to turn around.

If you are operating the 'separation at night' technique she will be pretty full in the udder and probably very pleased to be milked. A new mother which has not been hand milked before might be ticklish and jumpy so you must be patient and kind but positive in your actions. Be aware that she may dance around a bit and your first attempts may not be successful, resulting in much spilled milk but hopefully no tears! Whatever you do DON'T LOSE YOUR TEMPER! Angry goats can be demonic!! A stressed goat will not let down her milk without a fight and udder damage can ensue.

Try to be as relaxed as possible and feed the goat her concentrates to get her to be likewise. Milking animals become 'conditioned' to letting down their milk and so a routine sequence is important. Once the sequence is established the goat will be very easy to milk indeed.

Rinse your hands in the sterilising bucket and wet one of the cloths. Thoroughly wipe the udder or wash it if required. Repeat the process with the second cloth. If the udder is clean, the cloth will be too. With another cloth, dry the udder.

Put a small amount of udder cream onto your hands, rub it in and then rub it onto the udder. This is just to moisturise it so it shouldn't be too greasy.

You now need to check the milk on both udders before you begin milking in earnest.

Gently take two or three 'squirts' from the first side into the plastic cup. If it is clean and white with no lumpy bits or blood stains it is fine. Discard this and do the same on the other side. Assuming that it is OK too you can proceed with the milking.

Use your right hand for the udder nearest you and your left hand for the one furthest from you. If this is a novice milking goat or if you are milking for the first time you may prefer to milk one side out at a time. Obviously this is going to be more time consuming, but until your confidence (or the goat's confidence) grows, you may find it easier.

How to do it!

The actual removal of milk from the udder should be easy. It is a knack, and once learned is never forgotten. For the purposes of instruction, I am going to explain how to use one hand.

Put your four fingers together and lay them around the teat. Gently but firmly close your fingers around the teat to connect with your thumb and squeeze in a slightly downward motion. If nothing happens just keep trying. You will feel a mild resistance in the teat and this will be the point at which the milk is beginning to travel down the milk duct. The whole process is a psychological one as it is a reflex response in the goat which follows stimulation by the milker. This can even be a visual response on the part of the goat that recognises the routine. The reflex is transmitted in part by the nerves and partly by the release of the hormone oxytocin which acts on the alveoli of the udder which contain the bulk of the milk and squeezes the milk into the gland cistern. Once you have achieved the goal once it will become easier every time until you can milk the goat in just a few minutes.

The process of milking is simply pressure and release. As you release the pressure the cistern refills, as you apply pressure the milk exits through the teat. When I had vet students on my holding in Norfolk in order to help them with the handling and milking of dairy animals, I had a practice technique which involved getting a rubber glove and tying the thumb and all but the middle finger at the palm point with elastic bands. I then made a small pin prick on the end of the middle finger and filled the glove with warm water, after which I tied up the top. Try 'milking' the finger on the glove. The technique is similar!

So; assuming that you can now empty one side of the udder, progress to the second side. Then, finally, use both hands together, one on each teat.

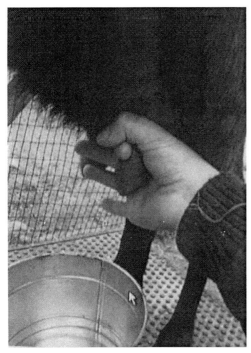

'SQUEEZE!'

Cover your milking bucket and put it to one side. Once you have dealt with the goat, get the milk to the house and strain and refrigerate it as soon as possible.

When you have finished, dry the udder with the last cloth, apply more udder cream to your hands and give the udder a good coating by gently massaging in.

You can now return the goat to her kids and they will finish off the job for you because your first few encounters will not necessarily empty the udder fully.

An average dairy goat should give you between 3 and 4 pints of milk every morning using this technique. The kids' constant daytime feeding will stimulate her to produce plenty of milk.

She will need up to a kilogram of dairy mix each day on this regime in order to support what is a fairly high demand for milk. By the time the kids are four months old they may not necessarily be taking everything the doe produces during the day, particularly if there is only one kid, so you may have to 'strip out' again in the evening. I have only had one goat in 37 years of goat keeping who has ever needed this as milk is produced very much on a supply and demand basis.

MAXIMISING YOUR MILK SUPPLY THROUGHOUT THE WINTER

When autumn approaches winter is not far behind and it's time to consider how best to provide the appropriate nutrition for your dairy goat to ensure a constant supply of milk throughout the winter. This is particularly important if you are not planning to mate her again this year and want her to 'run through' until next year.

If the kids from this year are not yet weaned, now is the time to do so by October, assuming they are around 16 weeks old and you have been following the regime of 12 hours with mother and 12 hours separated, as suggested for those who have work commitments throughout the day. If you separated them soon after birth, then weaning will have taken place in any case.

If the kids are still with their mother for part of the time, they must now be separated. The doe will be very happy to be given a rest and the kids will be well established in their own right and will no longer be dependant on their mother's milk. I know that some breeders continue to supplement their kids with bottles for several months longer, but I have never found this to be necessary and it will simply create more work for you.

If your kids have been with your goat for part of the day you may need to milk at either end of the day in the short term. It is important to completely strip the udder at least once a day to keep the milk supply. It is all about supply and demand. The more you milk, the more the goat will produce, within reason.

Assuming that you have a dairy goat of good milk lines she will be producing, during full lactation, anything from 5 to 8 pints of milk a day. Inevitably, as time goes by, during that period of lactation the yield will naturally begin to drop. We must remember that the goat is producing milk very much as nature intended for the feeding of her offspring. Nature did not intend her to feed her offspring until they are as big as she is and so her milk supply will diminish once the kids are of weaning age. In the wild state this would be anywhere from 4 to 12 months of age and so, for our domesticated goat to continue what is effectively an unnatural lactation period, we have to provide support with both management and food.

Many things must be considered when 'running through' a dairy goat as follows:

WORMING (see Chapter 3 for details)

Whatever your worming programme, your dairy goat needs to be wormed regularly and you MUST observe milk withdrawal periods as dictated by the manufacturer. All milk during this withdrawal period must be discarded. Do not give it to other livestock, but make sure you milk as normal or the yield will drop and disappear completely. Your worming programme should be very clear in your mind and written down so that you do not forget how you are going to manage the rotation of products. You should discuss with your vet how and what preparations you are going to use to maximise effectiveness and wormer resistance. If you use organic wormers then this is also the time to have a worm count done. Used according to advice these wormers should be very effective but an annual worm count will reassure you. Again, discuss this with your vet.

VACCINATION

Vaccination should also be done around this time, if it is due.

AVOID WORMING AND VACCINATION AT THE SAME TIME

The reason for this is that giving both at the same time can create a stress reaction in the goat and lower resistance to other infection, cause scour and as a result reduce the milk supply, which will never recover. Also the effectiveness of any vaccine relates to the good health of the animal at the time it receives the vaccine.

A preparation such as Heptavac P Plus is the ideal vaccination for goats as it immunises them against dysentery (this affects kids more than adults), pulpy kidney, struck, tetanus, braxy, blackleg, black disease and clostridial metritis. Assuming that your goat has already received a standard course of this vaccine, you will need to vaccinate annually only. If not, then a course of 2 injections which are given four to six weeks apart will set her on the right course. Any kids which are being retained or sold on should also receive an initial course of this vaccine.

THERE IS NO MILK WITHDRAWAL PERIOD FOR THIS PRODUCT.

RAISING GOATS

BLUETONGUE VACCINE - BTV8

Eventually the whole country will be able to access this vaccine, but currently only Surveillance and Protection Zones have been issued with it. You will be sent a letter from the Animal Health Office once the vaccine is available in your area. You should order the quantity you require and absolutely no more than that from your vet. Sheep and Goats only require one injection of 1ml to be given under the skin (subcutaneously).

THERE IS NO MEAT OR MILK WITHDRAWAL PERIOD FOR THIS PRODUCT.

Make sure you enter ALL medicines administered in your Animal Medicine Record Book.

NB. ALL AND ANY VACCINES SHOULD NEVER BE GIVEN TOGETHER AND A PERIOD OF 2 WEEKS SHOULD ELAPSE BETWEEN EACH.

NUTRITION OF THE LACTATING GOAT

To help maintain a good milk supply and keep the goat in good bodily condition, you will have to address her diet through the advancing cooler months of the year. Hopefully she will have had a good supply of grazing and browsings throughout the summer months and you have kept an eye on her condition, so she should really be looking her best right now. Whether she is to be housed, part housed or living out with shelter through the autumn and winter, the nutritional value of herbage drops quite dramatically after July and, although there is often a flush of growth during October, you will now have to supplement her food in order to maintain that milk supply.

She should be receiving an ad lib supply of the best hay you can find at all times and whether she lives in or out, the hay should not be fed on the ground. She will require 2 to 4 feeds of concentrates a day if that is possible. If you are only able to feed twice a day, reduce the concentrate ration slightly and add some Alpha A to it instead. This is because large concentrate feeds can result in the goat developing acidosis. Use a proprietory goat mix or a goat dairy mix if you can find one. A standard goat mix is fine, but add some dairy nuts to it, bringing the weights up to the following:

> ❋ 2 feeds weighing 1lb each plus a double handful of Alpha A in each

OR

> ❋ 4 feeds a day of 10 oz each plus a single handful of Alpha A in each

You can also add chopped fruit and vegetables, banana skins and stale bread which has been oven baked, but legally nothing that constitutes 'catering waste' and on no account anything that might have meat traces or animal fat either on or in it. She will also require clean water which is changed at least daily and, if possible, warm water when she comes in at night and a mineral block manufactured for goats.

DO NOT USE SHEEP PRODUCTS - THEY DO NOT CONTAIN COPPER AND GOATS HAVE A COPPER REQUIREMENT.

Use the herbs you may have dried through the summer, crushed and added to the feeds. Nettle in particular is thought to be helpful with milk production.

Essentially, your goat will thrive and be productive on a regular routine, good forage and, in particular, long fibre as is found in the best quality meadow hay.

MIND SET

The final consideration is your goat's mind set. This may sound odd, but a happy and contented goat is a productive one.

! Make sure her recently weaned kids are somewhere where she can see them.

! Do not isolate her from other goats

RAISING GOATS

!   Human interaction is important. Talk to her whenever you pass.

!   Make sure you and others are calm and considerate around her at all times, and never raise your voice.

!   Be patient and kind at all times, even if you are in a hurry.

!   Attend to any minor ailments as soon as they are spotted.

!   Keep her warm, dry and draft free.

!   Make sure she has a plentiful supply of clean forage and water at all times.

Provide a radio in the goat shed if possible, preferably not playing loud pop or dance music as the persistent 'thumping' can be distressing to herd animals as they perceive it to be the galloping of a fleeing herd.

DAIRY GOATS AND A FULL TIME JOB

Most of us who aspire to be smallholders have to support our efforts with some kind of paid employment. Our smallholding may well be productive and support all or some of our family needs, but, with the odd very rare exception, we will have to support our activities with earnings from a different source. If your smallholding is essentially animal free then there is no problem at all. Some animals can do very well with only a few minutes attention during the week and then a more concerted effort at the weekends, but what if you want a dairy animal that needs milking at regular intervals? I am going to address how one person can keep a dairy goat while working '9 'till 5.'

Let us assume that you are working and running 2 dairy goats and their kids and goatlings from perhaps the last kidding and the year before. (A kid being this year's offspring under the age of 12 months and a goatling being last years offspring over 12 months but less than 24 months).

The various permutations of this could be endless, but this is to offer guidelines on what you might otherwise think is impossible, with or without children being an additional factor.

Milking goats need to be kept to a good routine if they are to perform to their maximum ability and remain healthy and happy. All animals, just like humans, thrive on a good regular routine and by getting your animals into a good pattern of care you will find that your own routine and organisational skills sharpen up too. After many years of children (six children over a 32 year span) and animals (too many to begin to count!) I have discovered that the two psychologies are inextricably linked and recently I have also had to think about my aged mother prior to her sad demise, I found the child/animal psychology worked a treat in that department too!

One of the most important things is to make sure you are around when the goat expects you to be, so plan your day on paper from Monday to Friday and make sure you stick to it and have a contingency plan if things go wrong.

Assuming that you have to allow an hour to get you and whoever else ready for work/school in the morning, work backwards in chronological terms from the time you must leave your home. Likewise, when working out the times you need to feed/milk at the other end of the day, work forwards from the time you leave work, factoring in the journey, collecting children etc.

Ideally a dairy goat needs to be milked twice a day with 12 hours in between, but it is possible to get away with milking once a day if there are kids (the goat variety).

If you are going to milk twice a day you will probably need to allow 30 minutes to 'do' the goat, including feeding, watering, washing the udder, milking, taking the milk to the kitchen, straining and depositing it in the fridge. In the evening, of course, you can do it all at your leisure!

So, if you leave for work at eight o'clock, allow yourself an hour for organisation and 30 minutes for the goat, so you will need to be outside and ready to go at 6.30 am. If you have more than one goat to milk, allow another 20 minutes for that one.

RAISING GOATS

Likewise, in the evening you might be able to milk by 6.30pm, but don't worry if it is 7.30pm. Just try to keep those times the same every day.

MY PREFERRED METHOD

If you have goat kids at foot, then you will have a much easier scenario. Let the kids stay with the doe for twelve hours of every day. You can decide what you would rather do. If you prefer to milk in the mornings, separate the kids from the mother overnight and put them nto a pen where they can see each other, but not touch. If you have goatlings and the kids are over 6 weeks old they will be happy in the goatling pen overnight. By this time they will be nibbling hay and eating concentrates and browsings and not worrying unduly about Mum. I would suggest that they stay with the doe 24 hours a day for the first two to three weeks before you start the separation. If you prefer to milk in the evenings, operate the reverse scenario and keep them separate during the day.

When the kids are on the doe they will very adequately milk her and will probably increase the milk supply as a result of their constant demands on her. You will have a very full udder to milk at the end of the twelve hour period and get a good quota of milk. When operating on this regime I always leave a little milk in the udder for the kids after I have taken what I need or else they can get quite rough and aggressive with her.

IN OR OUT?

The above regime is for goats who are kept housed. For goats who live out I think you would have to operate a regime where the kids were separated during the night by penning them in an enclosed building so that they could be free to run and graze during the day. Personally I think dairy goats are safer housed at night, particularly kids, and would always recommend this. My Angora goats have always lived out with shelter but I have never released kids to the outside world until they were at least ten days old as they are quite small and vulnerable. It is slightly different for dairy goats as a general rule as the kids tend to be larger and bolder, but they are still vulnerable to foxes and dogs.

HOW LONG CAN I DO THIS FOR?

Most kids will feed from their mothers for as long as the doe permits it. In my experience this is between four and six months, although I have had does which are quite happy to let their goatling daughters feed from them when well over a year old. Your goat will let you know on this one.

Using whichever of the previous methods suits your own individual requirements, you should be able to survive on milking once a day for around six months. Ideally then this is the time to start your twice a day milking regime, or if you find the doe's yield beginning to drop you can then carry on milking once a day only. Be warned though, from this point forward it is likely to be milk reduction all the way and you will want to consider mating her again fairly soon.

THE TIMING OF MATING AND KIDDING

The timing of mating your goat is all important for fitting into your milking plans. Traditionally the rut for goats in the Northern Hemisphere has been between October and February, but in these days of a warmer climate I have found most goats are coming into season and ready to mate from June to April, which obviously gives you a much larger window from which to choose your mating times.

You should bear in mind that gestation is 5 months, give or take a day or two. Ideally you want your goat to kid in the early spring when the flies are not yet up and the grass is beginning to grow, although much will depend on the part of the world in which you live. I always try to have my house goats non-milking and heavily pregnant through the worst months of the year in order to minimise my winter work and time outside in poor weather. I aim to kid my house goats in March, letting the kids have the milk throughout that month whilst still housed 24 hours a day. I then separate them at night, milk the goats in the morning and turn them out in the day time with shelter on good days with the kids at foot. The kids will do 50% of the work for you until June at the least and maybe through to August if you want them to, but you will have longer days and perhaps want to end the twice a day milking yourself, depending on your milk needs. So you will need to have your goat mated in November to achieve

RAISING GOATS

this. By September of the kidding year you will have to be your own master with regard to the milking and, if you decide to opt for once a day, you can expect the milk supply to dwindle to nothing by Christmas. Is this a problem? Well no, not really, because there is no reason why with good care you can't mate the goat every year and so the whole process will begin again by choosing a November mating once more. You will still be able to milk your goat through to January or February if you keep up the regime because she won't need to be dried off until she is eight weeks away from kidding. If you have two dairy goats you could breed from them in alternate years and let them have a year off if you prefer. Also remember that last year's kid is this year's goatling and she too could be ready to mate in the autumn of her second year aged 18 months old or even before she is well grown.

WILL THERE BE ENOUGH MILK?

Most good dairy goats will produce six to eight pints of milk a day whilst in full lactation which is far more than the average family needs, even if you are making cheese and yoghurt. Shared with the goat kids you can expect to achieve half these rates.

Goat's milk freezes perfectly well with virtually no detriment to the quality and so you can freeze a plentiful supply for the weeks you may be without fresh milk. Freeze it in plastic bags or used plastic milk containers that have been properly washed and sterilised with dairy hypochlorite or household bleach and then thoroughly rinsed several times.

Goat's cheese, once matured and then frozen, will keep for up to five years in a freezer with no detriment (astounding but true - I have some!) and I have kept frozen goat's milk for up to two years and frozen yoghurt for a year.

PLANNING

The Daily Routine (morning milking)

6.30 am. Feed all goats with hay and concentrates - just give a tiny amount of the dairy goat's ration to her at this stage as she will need the rest while you milk her.

Add clean bedding and give fresh water to all goats

Move milking goat to clean area for milking, give concentrate ration, wash udder and milk.

Cover, milk and return goat to pen.

Put milk in a safe place ready to return to house.

Return your goat to the pen or paddock and put the kids back with her. Don't worry if the kids get noisy while you are working or milking, it is just anticipation of the return to Mum. She will only let them feed for a few minutes before getting on with her own life. They will then return to her at frequent intervals throughout the day for top ups. Take note how she will stop, regurgitate and chew cud while they are feeding (if you have the time!!).

7.00am. Return to the house with the milk, strain and store it in the fridge and get on with YOUR life.

6.30pm. Do the whole thing in reverse but bypass the milking!

7.00pm. Get on with YOUR life!
For evening milking you will need to separate the kids during the day instead.

RAISING GOATS

A Workable Routine for Mating and Milking

JANUARY	ONCE OR TWICE A DAY MILKING
FEBRUARY	DRYING OFF
MARCH	GOAT NOW DRY
APRIL	KIDDING MONTH
MAY	SEPARATE KIDS FROM DOE FOR 12 HOURS A DAY AND START MILKING
JUNE	ONCE A DAY MILKING
JULY	ONCE A DAY MILKING
AUGUST	ONCE A DAY MILKING
SEPTEMBER	ONCE A DAY MILKING
OCTOBER	ONCE A DAY MILKING
NOVEMBER	GET THE GOAT MATED - DON'T MILK ON MATING DAY, LET THE KIDS DO IT.

(The milk MAY be tainted for perhaps 2 or 3 days after mating, but with careful udder washing this should be overcome by day 4 at the latest).

EXCESS MILK SUPPLIES AND WHAT TO DO

Despite your best efforts to manage all that extra milk you may still find yourself with a glut and wonder what to do with it. Legally (see Chapter 1) you cannot give it or sell it to your friends or relations without first obtaining a commercial dairy production status via the various agencies set up to govern food hygiene in the UK. You may think that no one will know.......well, they probably won't, BUT you only need to get the hygiene wrong once and if somebody gets food poisoning questions will be asked and the next thing is that you may find yourself being fined or worse. If you feel you want to provide dairy products to anyone at all then consider getting the appropriate approvals. It is not difficult; you can sell as little or as much as you want in the certain knowledge that all is well and you are not breaking the law. You will also have the additional comfort of knowing that the produce given to your family is safe and wholesome.

GOING COMMERCIAL

Taking the next step with your goat herd

STAY AHEAD OF THE REGULATIONS

It is easier than you may think to sell your goat's milk legally and safely to the general public. As previously stated you cannot legally give, barter or sell you goat's milk to anyone outside your immediate family (technically, if you take the regulations literally, it is actually illegal to give the milk to your family too without approvals and so, if it is your intention to become a 'commercial herd' however small, it pays to be on the right side of the law before you begin. Once identified as a 'Regulation Dodger' within the various agencies relating to agriculture and environmental health, you will find that your reputation will go before you and you will encounter numerous problems. My advice to anyone with regard to animal and food regulations is to be a step ahead of the current regulations and to be able to quote them chapter and verse if challenged.

Remember that regulations exist not to make your life difficult but to make sure you, your animals and the general public stay safe and that nothing untoward gets into the food chain.

WHERE TO START

Your first port of call should be to your local Environmental Health Office. Speak to your local officer and ask to be sent a copy of the Dairy Regulations. These can also be obtained online.

He/she may offer to visit to give advice, but I would suggest you read the Dairy Regulations first because you will then have an understanding of the various rules and what will be involved in order for you to get the necessary permission to start selling your produce to the public. In time, once you have satisfied the hygiene requirements of the EHO (Environmental Health Officer) he will approach the Dairy Hygiene Inspectorate on your behalf and set the wheels in motion.

RAISING GOATS

HEALTH, HYGIENE AND THE DAIRY REGULATIONS

Once you have a copy of the Dairy Regulations don't be daunted by its rather robust contents - they are aimed at large farming concerns which are probably far more complex than your own smallholding set up. Because all food producers, however small, need to be singing from the same song sheet, all food regulations are 'universal' so you have to be producer specific when taking them apart. I would suggest that you go through them with a highlighter pen to ascertain which bits relate to you and your proposed enterprise.

The ones that are really going to affect you are the need to have a clean area which has a separate air space to that in which your goats live.

The requirement to exclude poultry, dogs and cats from in or around this 'clean' area.

The requirement to be able to handle your milk in an area that is not your kitchen area. This will not mean that you have to rebuild your home, but it should be quite easy to modify what you have in order to comply.

The rules are actually very sensible and if you produce dairy products from your animals for your family you should be fulfilling this requirement anyway to eliminate any risks to their health. In response I can hear you saying "But I've been drinking milk from Gertie and Daisy for the last five years AND milking her in her stall and I'm fine!" but remember that when we live in a farm or smallholding environment, we tend to obtain a degree of immunity to some of the "bugs" that emanate from our home produced food. Of course this will not be the case for our potential market in the outside world, so here we have to be super responsible.

So, a separate milking 'room' is obligatory. When I first started my commercial herd I ran the goats out of a timber stable block which had a tack room attached. The tack room shared the same air space as the stables so I installed a false ceiling, white emulsioned it and sealed the concrete floor with concrete paint and we were there. The walls need to be scrubable or hoseable and so you will need to use the appropriate paint - remember that mine were timber walls.

If you have solid construction walls it becomes easier. I did need to repaint the walls twice a year to make sure they remained waterproof, but if the walls are solid, once a year should be sufficient. The key to success is making sure that you can keep the interior hosed or washed out after every milking time. You could even use a small garden shed which is separate from where the goats are, but not too far away (consider moving it?), is not used for anything else and has a solid floor. Remember we are smallholders, ever resourceful and able to make something out of nothing, so use your imagination and view it all through an Inspector's eyes!

The next step is to confirm that your goats are fit and healthy and can provide a clean milk sample. This will be tested before you are able to sell your milk and will also be tested regularly thereafter. An Environmental Health Officer will call on a regular basis and take a random sample, usually in the receptacle you sell it in. You will be contacted if there are any problems. Like most things, 'no news is good news.'

When you are inspected the officer will want to watch your milking routine to make his all important Risk Assessment and advise if there are any perceived problems. There should be no problems with your hand milking and in many ways this is easier when you first start off with one or two goats. As time goes by you may want to consider a small milking machine. However, this does involve a lot more cleaning! Young hands cope well with milking up to five goats twice a day, but older ones very soon suffer with carpel tunnel syndrome and tendon problems, so be warned!

ESSENTIAL BASIC EQUIPMENT

As a bare minimum for your embryonic business you will need only a few basic essentials and if you only wish to supply friends and family you will probably need no further investment.

2 stainless steel lidded buckets
1 stainless steel milk strainer
Filter papers
Dairy wipes

RAISING GOATS

Dairy Hypochlorite
A fridge kept specifically for milk
A fridge thermometer and a temperature control book
A dairy thermometer
Milk cartons and lids
Labels (these can be home made)
A utility room with a bowl and a half sink OR separate wash basin.

If your utility room (which is about to become your dairy) has a washing machine/tumble drier in it, then it is best if you can move this. However, if you can show your Environmental Health/Dairy Hygiene Inspector that you can safely handle your milk with a time separation between the laundry usage of the room and that the working areas are sufficiently clean and treated with hypochlorite or something similar, they will usually not have a problem with this. This room must be designated as a 'clean' room and no dogs, cats, dirty vegetables, wellies etc. can be kept there.

It may sound complicated, but it actually isn't and you have got to want to make this work if you are going to succeed.

WHERE TO OBTAIN THE NECESSARY EQUIPMENT

Obtaining the appropriate equipment is easy. Either use the internet, telephone a supplier such as Goat Nutrition (see the Resource Section) or check out auction sites such as eBay for the things you need.

Labels for your product can be home made on a computer or you can go to a specialist labelling company.

You will need to communicate with your local Trading Standards Office (you will already be familiar with this from your Animal Movements) as to the current legislation for your labelling. It is better to get it right from the start rather than have to repeat it again later.

WHAT ELSE DO I NEED TO KNOW?

If you sell from the farm gate you will not to have to obtain a EU/UK mark (the little oval mark that you see on food from shops). If you want to sell at Farmers' Markets, via a third party or to the catering trade you will have to apply for this and then you will be inspected further and given a unique number which must be displayed on your product. If you expand your range you will have to seek further approvals.

You CAN sell your milk unpasteurised and in my experience most people who want goats milk DO NOT want it pasteurised.

If you feel pasteurisation is safer (some EHO's will try to persuade you that it is better, but don't be pressurised if you believe you are doing the right thing - your milk sample will be the proof of the pudding!) then you will need to buy a small pasteuriser. Be prepared to spend a couple of hundred pounds on a new one.

YOUR GOATS

Make sure that you have at least two goats who are producing six to eight pints of milk each day and that they are healthy, happy and easy milkers with good udders. If they fulfil the criteria of the first sentence of this paragraph, the rest will be academic anyway! Your goats should be spending a good period of the day on good grazing and should have first class stall accommodation with each pen at least six feet square. They should be cleaned out daily if possible and have scrupulously clean bedding and floors.

ECONOMICS AND VIABILITY

Before you start, work out the economics for you and your family. Be sure that your management of your dairy goats will enable you to supply the needs of your customers. If you let them down once you may lose them forever.

Be prepared to embrace the fact that you will have to milk twice a day 365 days a year unless you have a trained person to take over and accept that you may have to cull or re-home any dairy goats that do not produce efficiently.

RAISING GOATS

Understand that you will have to breed from at least one female annually in order to keep your supply consistent.

You will also have kids to dispose of every year and you must take responsibility for their ultimate fate. Most herds find the ratio of males to females is greater and that will involve castration and the rearing of goats for meat (see Chapter 5) or humane destruction by your vet within a few days of birth. NEVER pass them on to an unknown source.

IN SUMMARY

Running a commercial dairy herd, however small, is a rewarding experience and you can produce a much need product with pride but farming on any scale is hard work and is badly paid in monetary terms but it does give a lifestyle craved by many and holds so many benefits which can never be counted.

CHAPTER 5

MEAT AND SKINS

WHAT SHALL WE DO WITH THE KIDS?

With your breeding does comes the benefit of milk for dairy production but with it, of course, comes the annual influx of kids. They are quite delightful if you just have a handful, but by the time you have progressed to a larger herd of say five animals or more, the dear little kids can turn into proverbial gremlins! It was at this point when I ran a commercial unit that sending the unwanted males to the abattoir once they were old enough became more of a relief than a sadness.

Goats, unlike sheep, need a lot longer to mature to a reasonable kill weight and, unlike lambs who will probably be ready at 22 to 26 weeks, a goat will be 6 to 9 months old, depending on its breeding.

Whatever rearing regime you use for your kids, the best start in life for them is to spend at least 2 weeks with their mothers and, from your point of view, up to four months if you don't want to become involved with bottle feeding.

If your goats are meat specific, for instance Boer goats or maybe Angora cross hybrids, then you won't be thinking about milk for the household and your goats can do the rearing of the kids for you. If you have essentially dairy goats and the kids are just surplus to requirements, then the 2 regimes are going to vary as follows:

MEAT SPECIFIC GOATS

MATING, KIDDING AND FEEDING

Your aim will be to try to arrange kidding to the time of year which gives your goats the best start in life and you the least expense in supplementary

RAISING GOATS

feeding.

Ideally, in the northern hemisphere, you will be looking to kid these females in April or May when the grass is growing vigorously, minimising the need to feed hay and concentrates. This means then that you must mate them five months in advance of this, during November and December. During their pregnancies they will have been fed well on the best hay and goat specific concentrates and either living out with good shelter or housed during the winter months.

At kidding time special care must be taken as regards feeding, birth preparation and post partum care. In depth guidance to kidding and feeding at this time is addressed in Chapter 7.

You may decide to keep some or all of the female kids for further breeding, or at least keep your options open for them in the first year. Much of this will depend on how much space you have for your enterprise. Those female kids that you run on until the next year have several options. They could be sold to other breeders for pure or cross breeding, but remember that they are never going to be dairy goats, so don't even consider this or let anyone else consider it. They may become breeding stock for your own herd or finally, if none of the previous options prevail, it is not too late to send them to the abattoir for meat, even if they are 2 years old. Any goat over 2 years old is likely to be useful only for sausages, mince or burgers as the meat will become tough as the goat ages.

FEMALE KIDS

When the female kids are born check them for birth defects as soon as you can and tag them at 2 days old according to current legislation. You can keep up to date with this by visiting the Defra website. Keep an accurate record of which kids are the result of which mating and which doe and if they have any defects such as fish tail or double teats. Make sure that these go for meat however sweet they may be. The success of your breeding programme will be governed by this requirement, so be ruthless with regard to any birth defects.

All births and any deaths must be recorded in your Holding Register.

If your herd is at capacity and you do not have the right homes to which to sell these meat specific females, then you should not feel in the slightest bit guilty in sending them for slaughter.

Most Boer female kids command a good price though, so it is worth advertising them on the British Goat Society website or in a smallholder specific magazine first.

MALE KIDS AND BUCKS (BILLY GOATS)

You will almost certainly be sending all your male meat specific goats to slaughter. Occasionally you may be asked by another breeder for a goat kid to use as a terminal sire (a goat to produce offspring entirely for meat). Whatever their fate these kids must also be checked for birth defects and notes recorded of any producing mothers that have a problem. These kids will also need tagging according to current legislation.

Goat kids as young as 16 weeks (sometimes earlier) are capable of successful matings. You may already have a buck which you keep for use on your own herd and others perhaps, but every few years he will need replacing. Unfortunately if he is to go into the food chain at that time it is unlikely that you will want to eat the meat as it will have become very strong. The only option is to use it for dog food or to have him humanely destroyed by your vet and then sent for cremation. I always think the latter option is such a waste, but your own emotions will dictate the best way to proceed with this.

There is another option here and that is to use a goat kid or several goat kids on your various females year on year. If you do this then you must consider that ALL the offspring are for meat only as they are going to be closely bred to their mothers and therefore not a good prospect for further breeding by you or anyone else. It is this small gene pool of in-breeding which can create some of the worse birth defects in the next and future generations and it should be actively discouraged UNLESS, as previously stated, these kids all go for slaughter without exception.

Under no circumstances should a goat kid be allowed to serve more than four females in his first year of life.

RAISING GOATS

TO CASTRATE OR NOT TO CASTRATE?

Many people believe that castrating male kids can slow down their meat production growth. I have not found this to be the case. The only effect it can have is a short 'stop' in growth around the time they are castrated. If you are using the ringing method with lamb castrators this should be done legally before the kid is 7 days old. I prefer to both ring and tag on the second day of their lives. At this point it seems to cause them no distress and they return directly to their mothers and feed happily. Chapter 7 explains both how to tag and ring with minimal distress and risk of infection to your new born kids.

After this I think it can be extremely painful for them and surgical castration by a vet is far kinder. You would of course have to factor this cost into your profit scheme. Remember to make a note of all these male kids in your Holding Register too.

The problem if you leave the male kids entire is that by the time they are 12 to 16 weeks old you will have to separate them from their sisters and mothers as they are capable of mating them and certainly will if given the opportunity! Your females, even your female kids, could start to cycle again by July or August and if the kids were born in April - well, the rest is academic.

So castrated they can remain with their sisters and mothers until you are ready to take them to the abattoir. The mothers will naturally wean them sometime between 16 and 20 weeks of age, sometimes a little later. This will give the kids the best start in life and will save you the inconvenience and expense of supplementary feeding of dried goat's milk. They will have learned to eat at the trough with their mothers and should be thriving and happy. A happy, unstressed goat will make a good tender carcass and this is what this whole exercise is about.

Uncastrated means that all the boys will have to be separated from all the females and female kids before they are 16 weeks old, which means that some will be younger than that because of the kidding schedule. They will need supplementary feeding of concentrates and milk. The milk might be difficult because they won't be used to being bottle fed and are unlikely to start now. The option here then would be to combine milk pellets with their concentrates, but these will be cow's milk pellets which is not what goat kids are supposed to have!

You will need to put them somewhere out of sight and preferably out of earshot of the other goats or the distress caused will definitely cause them to back pedal on their development, putting them at risk of slower growth rates and infection caused by a stress depleted immune system. With a good feeding regime these goats should be ready for the abattoir by the time they are 6 to 9 months old.

NON-MEAT SPECIFIC GOATS

Young hybrid goats being reared for meat production

Much of the aforesaid relates to non-meat specific goats. These can be crossbreds or just dairy goat male kids and even female kids for which you have no breeding potential. You may decide to remove them from the dairy goat at a few days old and rear them on the bottle in order to gain the most milk from the mother. Personally I prefer to rear them using the 9 to 5 regime described in Chapter 4. This ensures that the kids grow well with minimal dietary upsets and reduces your own work load. Dried milk for kids is quite costly and will add £10 approximately to the rearing cost of each kid, so this needs to be given careful thought.

In every other way the regime will be the same. Some breeds may take a little longer to reach slaughter weight or you may have to accept a smaller carcase. Never let them feel any different to the rest of your goats; they deserve the same level of care as the rest of the herd including worming,

RAISING GOATS

foot trimming and vaccination. The cost of vaccination, particularly for clostridial diseases and Bluetongue is so low it is not worth taking the risk of neglecting these things and perhaps losing a kid at a few months old. Once weaned they can be reared in a group outside with shelter and supplementary feeding.

HOW, WHEN AND WHERE?

The slaughter of goats is the same as for sheep. They are stunned with an electric stunner which renders them unconscious and then they have their throats cut. It's graphic, but that's how it happens. If we eat or sell meat we must accept this and take on the responsibilities that go with it.

For these reasons it is so important that you take your goats to a proper EU registered abattoir and never ever consider letting someone have them 'on the hoof' to possibly slaughter illegally or by halal slaughter which is often done illegally or by inexperienced slaughter persons.

It is worth enquiring from others around you, for instance those with sheep, where they take their livestock for slaughter. Most abattoirs will be happy to show you around there premises and even allow you to witness the slaughter of the same or similar species as your own in order to satisfy any concerns you may have. Talk to them about the cuts of meat you can have and how it will be packed, how long you would like it hung before it is butchered and the time scale. Remember to ask about the skins if you want them and also about offal.

Ideally you will take your stock yourself because the goats will know and trust you and not be fearful. This is important for you and for them because, apart from the humane issues, any stressed animal that is slaughtered will produce tough meat because enzymes in the tightened muscles will affect the meat quality.

TRANSPORT

Your trailer, in order to comply with legislation, must have a metal floor and loading gates. You can put clean bedding in the trailer. The goats themselves should be clean and dry. This then may involve you housing them overnight before the morning they go to slaughter. If this is the case it is my advice that you bring them in for 2 or 3 nights beforehand to allow them to adjust to the situation and avoid unnecessary stress. Feed and water them as usual and supplement this with ad lib hay.

First contact your abattoir well in advance for a day and time to bring the goats in. Do this at least a month before you intend to go as at certain times of the year abattoirs are extremely busy and it can take a while to get a booking.
All animal movements must be supported with documentation and so, in advance of the day you go, fill in all the details required on the Animal Movement Form, making sure that tag numbers correspond to the animals that are actually going. You will need to state your animals' individual numbers, your UK Flock number, CPH number, your car registration number, your name and address, telephone number and the destination address of the abattoir. If you do not know the exact details of the final part, the abattoir will fill that in for you when you arrive.

You must also fill in the relevant part of your Holding Register to show what has happened to these animals and when. Not only is this a source of reference for you, and it's surprising as the years go by how quickly you forget who had what and when, but it is also a necessary regulation which helps with regard to the traceability of food, disease etc.

On the day you take the goats try to do everything as normal. Stay calm (it's always difficult the first time you do this, but it does get easier) and treat and talk to the goats as if it is just any other day. Remember, they have no idea what is going to happen so they do not see themselves as on death row. Sometimes being an animal does have its benefits as far reasoning is concerned!

Loading them onto the trailer should be straightforward if you have the necessary gates and they should meekly follow you up the ramp with a

RAISING GOATS

bucket of feed under their noses.

Once in, close the gates and the ramp and head off, trying to give them a good journey.
When you get to the other end do not unload them until you have been to the office with your paperwork. You will then be shown where to unload them.

The pens you unload into should have been cleaned out after their previous occupants. If not, question it and perhaps refuse to unload them until it is clean. There will be a Defra vet involved as they have to be checked once they are killed, so there is usually a very high standard employed. If you have any concerns about the abattoir you are using, then contact Trading Standards/Animal Movements with your concerns.

The goats will never be killed within eye shot of each other and the speed at which they are despatched is phenomenal. If there are several goats, more than one slaughter man will be involved. Remember that they are extremely experienced in the safe and humane handling of livestock and would never wittingly cause distress.

Some butchers and smaller abattoirs will collect from you and this can work well if you find the whole process of taking them difficult, or don't have an appropriate vehicle in which to take them. Once again, we are talking about very well practised people here and they do act with amazing professionalism and care.

BUTCHERING AND BAGGING

Wherever they go and however they get there, do make sure that they know what your butchery, packing and skins requirements are. Back it up with written instructions, attach it to your Movement Forms and keep a copy. Stress the length of time you want the carcasses hung. I would suggest 7 to 10 days for a goat carcass before cutting and bagging. Make sure that if you want the offal(heart/liver/kidneys) that you make that clear or you may not get them. If you want mince, sausages or burgers, discuss this with them too and the different flavourings that may be on offer. If you require gluten free sausages or burgers, then this can often be accommodated as well.

Your next job will be to collect the meat from your butcher or abattoir and the skins earlier if you are going to have them dressed.

The weights are going to vary from around 10kg killed out weight to as much as 20kg.

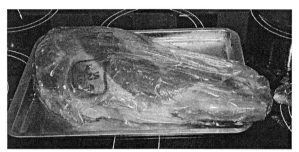

A leg of well produced goat

SELLING TO OTHERS

You can sell meat to other people by direct selling, but you must have permission to do this from Environmental Health. The animal must have been slaughtered and the carcase stamped by a registered EU abattoir and butchered according to Food Hygiene standards, then bagged and either frozen or sold fresh. It is an offence to do this without permissions but these regulations are not too onerous. If you are going to sell frozen meat your freezer facility will have to be inspected, but this usually involves the freezer being proven to remain below -16°C and being kept in a hygienic environment. If you are to take it to a Farmers' Market most EHOs (Environmental Health Officers) will allow it to be taken in polystyrene boxes, but some will insist on refrigerated boxes. Be aware that once even partially defrosted the meat cannot be re-frozen for resale. I normally take a small quantity with me and take orders for the following week. Some of the taken quantity I will sell, but the rest will go home for family consumption.

Find out what to do well in advance of the goats going to slaughter and make sure you have sufficient storage space for the amount of meat you are going to bring home. Otherwise make sure that people collecting their pre-orders for whole and half animals do so within an hour or so of your returning from the abattoir.

If you do not have sufficient freezer storage and have decided not to increase your capacity after considering the viability of getting more, then simply take your goats to the abattoir in smaller batches.

There is a good market for goat meat and it is very similar to lamb, but without the fat content often found in lamb and has a lower cholesterol content. It is in fact a very healthy alternative.

One other point worth bearing in mind and one that has helped me in the selection of breeding goats over the years is this. When you get your offal home, check it for abnormalities. By this I don't mean problems which make it unfit for consumption. Anything like that would have shown up at slaughter and you would have had a telephone call from the abattoir. The abnormalities I am speaking of are things such as unequal sized kidneys or enlarged hearts which could be a useful indicator as to the viability of certain members of your stock for breeding purposes.

A CAUTIONARY TALE!

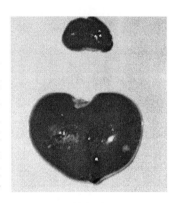

A pair of very well bred British Alpine dairy goats I had regularly produced male kids that went to slaughter. Several of these came back with differing sized kidneys and enlarged hearts. This was clearly a congenital fault that kept reoccurring. I knew the problem was not coming from my Toggenburg buck as he served all the females and it was only the British Alpine kids that had the problem. Therefore I knew the problem lay in the female line. A decision was made to only breed from these goats as producers of milk

Abnormal kidneys in a goat kid carcass

and all their kids would go to slaughter regardless of sex. This was not a problem as for three years they both produced triplet sons. Then on year four one produced the obligatory triplet sons and the other produced twins - a male and a female. A dilemma ensued. The female kid was so nice I decided to run her on and hoped for the best. When she was a goatling of about 16 months she was playing in the field with kids and goatlings and they were leaping and jumping for fun. Suddenly she jumped in the air and just dropped like a stone. When I got to her she was dead. I was confident that she had a heart abnormality and had died from heart failure. It was quite upsetting but I decided to have a post mortem done. She had the two differing sized kidneys and the enlarged heart and had died from a rupture of the aorta so my first instincts about progressing the breed line had been correct. Now I always act on instinct and have the intelligence not to breed from lines such as these. All the goats were quite closely 'line bred' which to some would mean 'in bred' but many goat keepers would disagree with me on this statement. I believe that it was this close line breeding which had caused the congenital defects that these goats suffered from. Neither of the adult females lived to a great age I might add.

FABULOUS GOAT SKINS: USING THE WHOLE ANIMAL

I have already taken you through the stages of rearing and taking your surplus kids to the abattoir and beyond. We will now look at using 'the whole animal' when it comes to effective use of the carcase.

I hope you will have opted for collection of the skins from your abattoir. In theory they will need a Movement Licence to accompany them to the tannery, but the tannery will advise you how they want the skins transported. My own choice of 'dressers' for my skins is Devonia Products in Devon. They are one of the few companies remaining in the UK who still operate a traditional tannery. You do not need to live in or even near Devon as the skins can be sent by carrier to this company. They are extremely helpful and a phone call will provide all the details you need. DO this BEFORE your kids go to the abattoir because, unlike the meat which you should ask your butcher/abattoir to hang for five to ten days, the skins need to be handled quickly. If your animals are killed at home this company will also advise you on how to proceed within the law.

If you have explained to your abattoir when you booked the animals in that you needed the skins for dressing, they should have done two things. The first is to have skinned the animals with great care and removed all the bits you don't want (I have received skins back with hooves and forelegs and worse still attached because I forgot to mention it, so be warned!). They should also have salted the skins and put them into an appropriate bag to await your collection. Sometimes they will make a small charge for the handling of skins but it is seldom more than £3 but do check this when you book the animals in. If you stayed with your animals whilst they were slaughtered you should be able to take the skins away with you as the process is pretty quick (in fact they will still be warm when you receive them). Alternatively, if you have left the animals at the abattoir for slaughter later in the day, ask when you can pick the skins up. Do this promptly as skins left in a warm environment for more than a few hours are likely to have deteriorated to the point of no return. It is important to extract as many of the natural fluids out of the skins as quickly as possible to prevent decomposition.

Once you have got the skins home, spread them out on a wooden pallet or something similar and rub them with course salt on the skin side, NOT the furry side. This can be purchased from most farm shops but if you have difficulty dishwasher salt will suffice, but it might be a more expensive option. Having done this to all of them you will then need to hang them out to 'dry' over a pole or a washing line. They should be under cover and away from risk or damage by vermin, dogs or cats. Also PLEASE do this and hang them out of the sight of living animals of the same type.

After a couple of days of repeating this process you can roll them up with the fur side innermost and pack them for sending to the tannery.

CARRIAGE AND PROCESSING COSTS

I usually put each skin into a white bin liner and the whole lot into a heavy duty black dustbin liner and then pack it into a sturdy cardboard box. If you don't make the package waterproof you may get leakage and this could delay or even stop the delivery of the parcel. You will need to use a 24 hour carriage service which will cost between £10 and £20 depending on the weight of your parcel. The cost of each skin for processing will be around £20. I have found I can sell good, well produced skins for £40 so the profit margin is really quite good. Some carriers ask what the content is and that can be tricky. Personally I use Interlink Express and they never ask that question. If you book your parcel online with any carrier the only question asked is size and weight. It sounds like this is some sort of illegal and clandestine exercise. It is not but some carriers get a bit upset when you tell them they are animal skins! All this is of course assuming that you are going to get someone to do the job. My skins are sold at Farmers' Markets and so I require complete traceability of any chemicals and processes used and so I opt for the professional touch which involves trimming and carding where required. The end results are usually outstanding and the demand is high, particularly for coloured skins. I process all my lamb skins in the same way. If you have only white skins the tannery can usually dye them in a wide range of colours if you wish. I usually find people will order a particular colour well in advance and are prepared to wait. Personally I prefer them to be natural, but it is a buyer's market and as smallholders we need to be acutely aware of this if we are to survive in the modern age.

DOING IT YOURSELF

If you want to process your own skins, this is perfectly possible but takes a little time. Because of traceability you will only be able to use these skins for your own use, but they make fantastic hard wearing rugs and smaller kid skins make fashion garments and cushion covers. Proceed in the same way as previously described, but on day three you will need to proceed as follows:

Approximately 35 litres of water
1kg broad bran
1kg non-iodised salt
2 plastic bins(150 litre size)
A stirring stick which needs to be about 4 feet long
500ml of battery acid (you can get this from an auto parts shop such as Halfords)
200g bicarbonate of soda
A wooden rack or stretcher (an old clean wooden pallet/s works well)
A can of Neatsfoot Oil
Nails
A wire brush
Sponge
Pair of thick rubber gloves and overall
(The quantities described will tan up to 6 goat skins)

RAISING GOATS

METHOD

Following on from the salting process described previously, let the skins dry out completely, ideally in a closed building and preferably laid flat on a pallet or similar. Move them daily so that the places where they were in contact with a solid object gets rotated round to allow the air to get to the 'wet' parts. They will end up like cardboard after anything from four to fourteen days depending on the weather conditions and temperature. Then soak the skins in clean fresh water until they are flexible again. This part of drying with salt and then soaking again is a vital part of the process, so don't try to bypass it!

Once soaked, you will be able to peel off the inner skin from the hide and discard it.

Next boil about 15 litres of water and pour it over the bran. Leave this to 'brew' for about an hour and then strain out the bran which will leave you with a brown coloured solution.

Put the salt into one of the bins and add the rest of the water, having brought it to the boil first. Stir it to dissolve the salt and then add the bran water and stir again.

When the solution is luke warm, add the battery acid. DO READ THE WARNING LABEL ON THE BOTTLE & ANY FIRST AID ADVICE. THIS IS NOT A JOB TO HAVE CATS, DOGS OR CHILDREN AROUND WHEN YOU ARE DOING IT!!

Pour the battery acid very carefully down the side of the container into the liquid to avoid splashing. Wear rubber gloves and protective clothing including eye protection. When this is done, gently stir the solution to mix all the ingredients together.

Add the skins to the solution and press down using the stick until they are completely covered and fully soaked. Leave for about 40 minutes, stirring from time to time.

Meanwhile, fill the other bin with clean, lukewarm water.

Next use the stick to carefully remove the skins one by one and put them into the clean water. Stir this around for five minutes or so and change the water when it looks messy. Repeat the process of rinsing. On this second rinse, add the bicarbonate of soda. This will neutralise the acid in the fur. The only drawback with this is that it will also neutralise the acid in the skins which to some extent can reduce the preserving of the skin. If the skins are going to be used as wall hangings, rugs or for craftwork I would not add the bicarbonate of soda but if they are going to be used for clothing, then I would.

Now you can remove the skins from the water. They will be pretty heavy and you will need to hang them over that pole again to drain. Once they have drained a little, soak the sponge in Neatsfoot Oil and apply it to the SKIN side of the pelt. This will be absorbed very quickly.

Now tack the hide to your pallet, pulling it to the desired shape without overstretching. Put it in a shady place to dry or back in the shed/building if the weather is unsettled.

Check the hides every day. Once they feel dry in the centre but still soft and flexible, remove them from the pallet with care and, fur side down, brush all over the skin side with the wire brush which will soften it. The colour will also change as it becomes 'sueded.' Now bring them indoors and finish by hanging them over a chair for a couple more days. Trim as required and Voila!

(I don't recommend this for sheepskins as they really do need to be professionally carded at the end of the process. Also washing them is quite difficult to do effectively.)

RAISING GOATS

WHAT ABOUT DISPOSAL OF TANNING LIQUID?

This is vital. Whether or not you decided to add the bicarbonate of soda to the process earlier, you must certainly add it now. It will create a powerful reaction and give off a potentially toxic gas, so add it and get out of the immediate area until the reaction has finished. It is best to do this outdoors but again with no children or animals about. It will now be neutralised and you MUST NOT pour it onto cultivated land or down the drain but if you water it onto driveways then, like a conventional weed killer, it will keep them weed free for some time.

This all sounds quite complicated but it is not and like all things, once you have done it a couple of times it becomes second nature. At all times be very aware of the potentially harmful effects of chemicals and act responsibly at every stage.

Most people I know try the self-dressing method at least once but like me they usually find themselves reverting back to the professionals. The profit margin maybe smaller but the convenience and certain knowledge that you will get back beautifully dressed skins in a couple of weeks can outweigh the financial disadvantages. Remember too that if you want to sell these skins then they simply must have been processed by a registered tannery.

Contact details for Devonia Products: 01364 643355

CHAPTER 6

GOATS FOR FIBRE

By fibre goats we mean any breed of goat that is kept for fibre or hair production. In the UK this generally refers to Angora, Cashgora or Cashmere. Some Angora herds support a number of Cashgora goats which are a 50% minimum outcross of Angora to a dairy breed.

ANGORA GOATS

Often mistaken for sheep by the general public but clearly goats, this breed makes as effective a scrub clearer as its dairy equivalent. It has a long curly coat and the fibre is known as Mohair, Angora wool actually coming from rabbits, not goats. The Angora doe will suckle her own kids, usually twins but occasionally singles or triplets and is not milked as she will require all her milk for the process of kid rearing. The Angora does require shearing if the fleece, which is a valuable commodity, is to be used. It is usual to shear Angora goats twice a year. However, if you do not want the fibre an Angora will self shed its fleece annually. The shed fleece is unlikely to have any monetary value or be of any use to spinners if this is the method employed as it gets dirty and cotted (tangled) in the shedding process.

CASHGORA GOATS

Showing 'hybrid vigour' this outcross makes an excellent meat carcass, being chunkier than a dairy goat with good hind limbs and shoulder, allowing bigger leg and shoulder joints when butchered. If the coat is not too course then it can be combed to produce a soft, spinnable fibre with many of the characteristics of cashmere. There won't be a lot of it and so this will be for yourself to spin or a hobbyist that you might know. True Cashgoras are Cashmere/Angora crosses but most people in the UK refer to a dairy goat/Angora cross as Cashgora

RAISING GOATS

CASHMERE GOATS

The Cashmere goat is a specific breed (see the picture in Chapter 2). Like the Cashgora its coat has to be combed to collect the fibre and the yield is not great which is why cashmere is such a valuable commodity.

WHERE TO START

If the idea of fibre producing goats is an attractive option for you then the Angora goat is the ideal goat for you. The first thing is to find yourself a reliable source to purchase your first animals. The Angora Goat Society will have a list of breeders with stock for sale. I would suggest that you purchase four does initially and an unrelated male kid. By purchasing the potential buck as a kid you will be able to make a friend of him from the outset. Angoras can be quite timid if they have been kept in a large herd, but they will soon become very tame with daily feeding and handling. If you just want a fibre herd for your own use, then four does will provide you with around 16kg of spinnable fibre every year and you may feel the need for a buck is not so important. One thing to be aware of though is that as the goat ages, the fibre will become coarser and less useable for spinning (particularly if you are planning to sell it) and so an older doe will only be useful for kid production as the years go by (or keeping that scrub well trimmed!). The first and second clip fibre from Angora goats is the most prized for its quality and softness.

A BUCK FOR YOUR HERD

Personally I think it is much easier to have your own buck and then you will have a closed herd with less risk of transmittable disease entering the herd. All Angoras have horns and a full grown buck will have big, beautiful curly horns but he won't use them on you if you have made a friend of him from the start. If you acquire him as a kid of 4 to 6 months he will be sweet natured and friendly. Handle him exactly as you would any other goat and he can run with his girls at all times. Nature will take its course and he will mate the does as and when.

Never, ever try to lead or pull a horned goat by the horns. It is painful and, especially in younger animals, they can snap and will bleed profusely. To lead your non-halter trained goat simply lift his or her chin in the cup of your hand, put a rope lead around the neck and walk forward.

MANAGEMENT OF THE BUCK

I have always run my Angora bucks with the females for 12 months of the year. A young, inexperienced buckling probably needs removing from the herd in the first year at kidding if the herd is kept outside as he may mistake imminent kidding as a sign of oestrus and become a dangerous nuisance to the doe at this time. I have found that by the second season (year) the young buckling will have 'wised up' to the situation and will simply observe the kidding without interfering. We tend to lose sight of how it all happens in the wild when we domesticate animals. However, you do need to have enough land if you are going to adopt this regime so that the doe can retreat to a quiet area to kid. The buck will generally keep an eye on things and watch for predatory animals such as foxes and protect the does and kids at this time. Since becoming a sheep keeper, I have adopted exactly the same sentiments with my rams and they have behaved the same way and so are no longer ostracized from their ladies at any time, unless I have to bring the ewes in for lambing.

DOES AND KIDS

On a free range system, adopting a sheltered arrangement for pregnant does and kids is wise. Angora kids are quite small when they are born and, depending on the time of year and your situation, it is wise to either bring pregnant does inside for kidding or to bring the newly born kids and doe in soon after birth and keep them inside for about ten days. If you have a barn or field shelter in the field, this can be achieved by penning within the barn or shelter. Putting some straw bales around the outside of the pen will help to give the doe privacy and will keep the kids out of draughts. Never put bales on the inside of pens as they can all too easily fall over and crush a young kid.

RAISING GOATS

MANAGEMENT OF THE FLOCK

Angora goats will live outside all year as long as they are provided with good shelter. Make sure that the shelter is big enough for them all to get into easily, or provide 2 smaller shelters. The tendency is for them to lie around the walls facing the outside. Angoras have strong natural instincts and one or two will often stand watch when the herd is resting. Like other goat breeds their coats are not waterproof and they can become saturated with water quite quickly and get chilled which leads to serious illness. They do not enjoy being confined in a goat house and are the wrong breed for you unless they can be free range for at least half of the year. Stocking rates should be no more than 6 goats to the acre. Beyond that you will run the risk of all the typical overstocking problems and be faced with a lot of supplementary feeding.

FEEDING

Feed good quality hay in a protected hay feeder from mid-October onwards or earlier if the usual October flush of grass is not there. This will depend on weather conditions and, of course, the availability of grazing/browsing generally available on your land. Remember that the sward needs to be at least 1½″ high to be suitable for the goats to graze effectively. They will also browse hedgerows if there are any, obtaining many nutrients from brambles, berries, perennial 'weeds,' leaves and twigs. If these browsings are not available then the feeding of other long fibre is essential and so a hay feeder should be kept filled at all times with either hay or a mix of top quality straw and hay.

Angora fleece grows at a rate of about an inch a month and this takes quite a large amount of energy from the goat. The quality of the fleece will reflect the quality of the feed.

As the grazing diminishes you will need to feed a proprietary goat mix once or twice a day. I usually work on 300g per goat per day; so considerably less than a dairy goat. The sulphur requirement for fibre goats of any type is greater than most other types of goat. Some proprietary goat feeds are Angora goat specific and Angora goat feed supplements are also available. A cheaper alternative is the addition of ½oz of Flowers of

Sulphur per goat per week. Mixed through the concentrate ration for the whole week this will improve the 'fleece' and help keep the goats free of worms and respiratory infections while also killing any feed mites which mite be present. This is especially true if you are using organic feed. Work the quantities out on a calculator or on paper to make sure you don't give too much. If you do the goats might scour for a day (pale in colour), but it won't harm them. Ideally you don't want any dietary imbalances with goats though so it is worth taking the time to work it out properly.

Provide a goat specific mineral/salt block in the field or field shelter at all times. It is better to place it under cover as the elements will erode it quite quickly and also the salts will kill the grass directly beneath it and beyond with water run off.

FENCING

Angoras are not climbers or jumpers and so a good strong sheep fence is perfect for them. Electric fencing is totally unsuitable as they are horned and can become entangled. Also, because of their heavy coats they insulate themselves very effectively against an electric zap!

ALL GOATS, AND THE ANGORA IS NO EXCEPTION, SHOULD NEVER, EVER BE TETHERED. ANGORA GOATS SHOULD ALSO NOT WEAR COLLARS AS THIS CAN SPOIL THE FLEECE!

HOOVES AND HORNS

Angora goats need their hooves trimming every six to eight weeks. The horn tends to be softer than that of other goat breeds and trimming is reasonably easy to do. Horns should be left alone. Do not disbud kids and never be tempted to cut bits off. Very occasionally a big buck might have an in-growing horn, but if this occurs consult your vet to have it cut back properly.

KIDDING

Usually quick and straightforward kidders, Angoras have not been

RAISING GOATS

changed much by managed breeding and their conformation remains as nature intended. With capacious bodies, short legs and a wide pelvis they manage to push their babies into the world with minimal trouble. The kids are quite small and if it is a winter kidding it is wise to bring both doe and kids inside for a few days while they establish themselves. By 7 to 10 days they are bold and strong and instinctively run to their dam if anything threatening occurs. They do not usually mis-mother their kids as some of the other goat breeds are inclined to do. If the doe has a heavy coat approaching the time of kidding it is sensible to clip away the long fleece around the tail and especially the udder as small kids can get entangled in long staples of the fleece. The fleece staple (strands) are very strong and it is possible for a kid to be badly damaged as a result. If you are unsure when to expect kidding then keep a close eye on the herd and as soon as the doe has kidded, scoop up the kids, holding them at your knee height and walk slowly to the 'confinement' shed with them. The doe will follow, bleating madly. Once inside you can deal with everything, including the removal of any fleece which is too long.

CASTRATION OF KIDS AND TAGGING

I always tag my kids on day 1 or 2 and ring any males on day 2. This MUST be done within the first 48 hours after birth. They do not even notice it then. After 3 days, in my experience, it can be painful and by day 7, the recommended limit, it is certainly very unpleasant indeed. If you are not practised at this job, find a stock keeper who is and do so well in advance of the event. Anyone with sheep will be able to do this for you. The wethered males can then be kept for fibre and grown on for meat or just kept as fibre goats for several years. Angora goats are subject to exactly the same rules as other goats and must be tagged appropriately. Currently that means 2 identical tags in each ear, one of which must be an EID tag (Electronic Identity Tag - see Chapter 1). If you do it well, the kids won't even notice.

TECHNIQUE FOR TAGGING

Put one across your lap in view of its mother with the front legs on one side of your knees and the hind legs on the other. Take the ear and find an area about mid-way up without a large vein. There is a very clear area where you can do this and it is not difficult. Apply the tag to one ear and then the other. The rules are that all goats/sheep over one year of age or for export MUST have 2 identical tags, one of which must be an EID tag. If it is a doe kid, you will doubtless be keeping her long term or selling her on, so 2 tags is the rule. If it is a male kid the same applies as you will almost certainly use him for fibre for the first year or two, even if his ultimate fate is the freezer.

PRODUCTION OF FIBRE

Known as 'The Diamond Fibre,' the mohair shorn from Angora goats has a wonderful lustre and is prized amongst all shorn fibres. Shear your goats twice a year. I usually do mine in April and late September but it will depend on the climate where you live. Do not leave your Angoras fleeceless once the temperature at night is consistently below 12°C. Most stock keepers are acutely aware of the weather conditions approaching, but sometimes the huge differential between daytime and night time temperatures in spring and autumn is overlooked. So be aware of that in your shearing calculations.

A sheep shearing machine is a suitable clipper but you can also use a good set of dog or horse clippers with a blade upgrade to something like a TDQ blade(Take Down Quick). A set of hand sprung sheep shears will also serve you well for a few animals and my recommendation would be a double bow shear, which is less stressful on your hands. Remember, you don't have to shear all of your goats on the same day! Spend a week getting them done if you need to.

Take time to trim their hooves at the same time and treat them for external parasites before you release them back into the field If you use a professional shearer who will shear your goats very quickly, it is fine to shear them in the same positions as used for sheep, but if you do them yourself you will inevitably take a lot longer and so a different position should be employed. The shearing pattern should be similar, but do them standing up, not sat down. A goat's internal organs do not like being kept in that position for long periods and they can become very distressed.

RAISING GOATS

If you have just a few Angora goats, half the enjoyment of keeping them is to shear them yourself and you will probably be using the fibre to spin and weave. If you have a lot the chances are you will be selling the fibre as unspun fleece or sending it to a small scale mill to be spun for you.

GET READY TO SHEAR

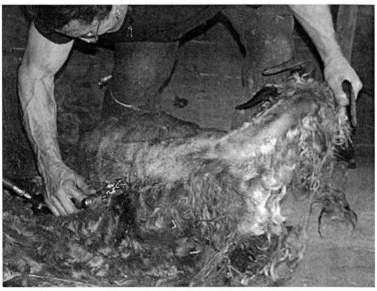

Shearing pattern for fibre goat

April is probably the best time to shear your Angoras and again six months later in early September, depending on which area of the country you live. The further north you are, the later you will probably shear in the Spring, so May and late September may be a better time for you. Make sure that you 'dag' your does before kidding though to allow the kids safe access to the udder unhindered by strands of long mohair staple. Dagging means simply trimming out the animal in vulnerable areas. Normally you would use a dagging shear which is like a hand sheep shear but with shorter blades, but you can equally well use a pair of sharp scissors or your electric clippers The worst case scenario for an Angora kid is either to semi-ingest a long piece of fleece while feeding or, worse still, to literally become strangled by it. They can also become entangled and be trampled as a result.

The second shearing should be done approximately six months later which relieves the Angora of a lot of hot clothing and also gives it time for sufficient regrowth before the colder weather begins. In colder climes it is sometimes better to house the goats during the winter months if the ground is frozen and snowy.

BEFORE YOU START

Make sure the goat/s are as clean as possible with no bedding attached to their coats. It is easier to pick and brush it out now rather than after the fleece is shorn

EQUIPMENT NEEDED FOR A FRUSTRATION FREE CLIP

A sharp pair of scissors/shears/clippers
Lubricating oil for the clippers and a soft brush to clean the blades
A large clean paper sack (a paper feed sack turned inside out is ideal)
A clean dry space with no bedding and good light
Proprietory anti parasitic application
Wound spray

If you only have a few goats then a good sharp pair of good old fashioned hand operated sheep shears will do the job for you. My choice is Burgon and Ball Shears which I find I can operate quite easily even with arthritic hands as they have a 'soft' spring. The double bow variety would be my first choice.

You can keep these shears sharp and in good order by purchasing a Burgon and Ball Shear sharpener for a few pounds. Keep the blades oiled after every use and store them in a dry place indoors.

Alternatively you can use a pair of dog or horse clippers with a TDQ or coarse blade. Some horse clippers will also take a sheep shearing head but can be heavy to use and great care must be taken not to nick the goats skin. If you should be unfortunate enough to do this, spray immediately with wound spray.

RAISING GOATS

WHERE TO START

Unlike a sheep, a mohair fleece will not come off in one piece and you should not try to do that. Start at the head end and work against the hair. If you are using hand shears grasp a hank of the fleece and cut about half an inch from the skin. That way your goat will look better and will also retain some fleece!

If you are using electric clippers do not take a second cut as you will end up with lots of short, unspinnable pieces. As you work through the coat put the good cut fleece into one paper sack and anything that looks overly cotted (tangled), dirty, soiled or otherwise contaminated with bedding, hayseeds etc. into the other. This will keep your working area clear.

With hand shears it might take you 30 or 40 minutes to complete one goat, but remember you don't have to do them all at once - take several days to complete the task if you like. With electric clippers it will probably take you 10 to 15 minutes. Personally I prefer the manual method as it is less traumatic for the goat and produces a better staple with no second cuts. Once you have finished the clipping process you can go over the goat for any missed bits and a general tidy up with shears or sharp scissors, which are easier for bits around the ears etc. We are all amateurs and no one expects a brilliant job the first few times! These extra pieces will have no use and should be discarded.

AMOUNTS OF FLEECE

The volume will vary depending on the age of the goat but can be anything from 1kg for a first shearing kid to 4kg for an older animal. As Angoras age, the quality of the fleece depreciates, but it is still useable for spinning, although it is less saleable on the open market. Kid fleeces, either the first or second shearing, are the most valuable. The fleece should have reached four to six inches long by the time it is shorn.

ANTI-PARASITIC TREATMENT

Use this opportunity to treat your goat with whatever anti-parasitic preparation you use. If your regime is organic or close to it use Flowers of Sulphur or Goat Nutrition's Delete carefully, applying it along the spine from poll to tail and keeping it away from the eyes . If not organic, use Spot On for sheep or one of the many other chemical sheep preparations on the market. Remember that most of them are not really licensed for use in goats. All chemical treatments need to be shown in your Veterinary Medicine Records Book (See Chapter 1).

Bear in mind that most spinners do not want a fleece that has had chemical treatments, so if you do use a chemical treatment you must observe the time restriction from treatment to shearing, which is normally four months.

Reward the goat for being such a good patient! Try not to laugh at its naked form! You will see what I mean when you get there. If your neighbours ask, just deny all responsibility!

DO I HAVE TO SHEAR MY ANGORA?

The simple answer is no, you don't. They will self shed in late spring to early summer. You might still be able to use some of the fibre but it will only be of use for domestic spinning. You will see the fleece begin to rise and peel off and over a period of days it will be as if the goat is stepping out of a big woolly jumper which will be deposited around the place, finally peeling off completely to leave a fine fuzz of new fleece underneath and a few 'guard' hairs over the middle of the back and sides. The better the standard of the stock, the less guard hairs there will be in the coat. These are the undesirable hairs for spinning but Angoras will have a proportion of these hairs as they get older. Known as kemp, the ratio will increase as the goat ages. Does can still be used for breeding when this point is reached and allowed to self shed. Wethers must then be considered as companion animals or freezer fodder.

SO WHAT TO DO WITH THE FLEECE?

If you are a hand spinner you will want to keep this for yourself and perhaps blend it with some sheep or even alpaca fleece for an interesting and beautifully soft yarn. You may want to spin it to create a beautifully fine yarn for shawls and stoles etc. The picture on P108 shows what can be achieved.

A selection of homespun and woven items and wool from mohair

Personally I blend mine with my Ryeland sheep fleece to make what is known as 'novelty' yarn. In other words it is spun by someone who is not very good and spins chunky stuff! However, it does make a lovely yarn which will create beautifully warm, washable and hard wearing sweaters for the smallholder! I have also experimented with a peg loom recently, weaving the fibre without spinning which is a worthwhile exercise, particularly for fleece from older animals with less value as spinning fibre. Peg looms can be bought online or in many craft shops and I recommend one that is about 50 inches wide so that it can be used to make rugs. You do not have to use the full width of the loom. Its other advantage is that it is the true 'cottagers' loom and does not need a large space to accommodate it. The weaving can be wrapped around it for storage and kept in a corner.

COMMERCIAL PROCESSING

If you have enough fibre then it is worthwhile having it commercially processed. Remember you can store your shorn fleece indoors for a long time in order to make up the quantities normally required by a commercial mill. You will normally require about 20 kilos for a mill to do a single run for you, but there are also share schemes operating where various producers can pool their fibre and share the yarn or even products produced from the yarn. Mohair fleece is highly prized for blending.

Providing it is clean and free from hayseeds and other debris, all mohair fleece has a value and can be sold through various outlets, including a scheme run by the Angora Goat Society - British Mohair Marketing. They will advise you of current prices and how you should pack and sort the fleeces for them.

Top grade mohair will be sold for use in clothes and suiting materials. Mohair is used for the production things as diverse as treadmills and conveyor belts too!

TO BREED OR NOT TO BREED

In these monetarily barren times, it is often sensible to consider the wisdom of breeding stock with an uncertain future. The greatest asset that the Angora has is the need to not cull out the male stock if your purpose is fibre. Wethers can be kept for fibre production year on year, later becoming pets or dare I say it-going in the freezer as above. If this is to be his fate, leave the final shearing and save the skin for processing to a rug. The meat of a four or five year old Angora will be very similar to mutton but with virtually no fat and the skin, properly and professionally processed will make a fantastic rug which you can keep or sell for anything between £80 and £120.

If you have no desire to grow the herd, then keep your female kids for replacement of older female stock and grow your wethers on to 18 months old. You will be able to take one or two shearings of the very best kid fleece, which is the most valuable, then grow on for six months to achieve a gorgeous rug and a good meat carcass as above.

RAISING GOATS

POINTS OF REFERENCE

- ❋ Angora Goat Society - email: Liz Graham secretary@angoragoat.fsnet.co.uk
- ❋ Commercial and Organic spinning -The Natural Fibre Company-website: www.thenaturalfibre.co.uk
- ❋ British Mohair Marketing-email as above
- ❋ Small scale spinning - Bob Tails - website: www.bobtails.biz
- ❋ Sprung hand shears - Burgon and Ball: website: www.burgonandball.com
- ❋ Clippers and Blades - Oster: website with links to suppliers: www.oster.com
- ❋ Anti-parasitics - Goat Nutrition Ltd: website: www.gnltd.co.uk
- ❋ Skin processing: Devonia Products, Buckfastleigh, Devon. No website but telephone 01364 643355

CHAPTER 7

Dealing with Illness and Veterinary Requirements

- Nursing the Sick Goat

- Poisonous Plants

STOCK WATCHING-THE SINGLE MOST IMPORTANT THING YOU CAN DO TO MAINTAIN YOUR GOAT'S HEALTH

Whether animals are out in the fields or in their sheds, the importance of stock watching cannot be over-emphasised. This is how we get the best indication how things are and how they might become become for our goats.

When you enter the goat house in the morning are they attentive and ready for action?
Are they eating all their food?
Are they drinking well?
Are their droppings how you would expect?
Are they scratching or biting themselves or each other?
Are their coats shiny and supple?
Have they got bright, clean eyes and dry, clean noses?
Are they lame?

In addition, if they are free range;

Do they look up and come toward you when you enter the field?

If all the answers to this are affirmative then you are doing a brilliant job and possibly deserve the stock keeper of the year award, but if one or two of them raise concerns then you must take steps to correct the problems before they become a crisis.

Raising Goats

Eating

If your goat is eating up all that is put before it, then things are probably going well. Just check her condition score: is she too fat or too thin? If she is really grubbing up then she may need a little more food and the best way to achieve this is with fibre in the form of hay and straw. If she is already quite portly and not in kid, then slow down her eating by again feeding more fibre, but of a lower quality. By that I do not mean bad quality forage, just one with less protein. For instance, if she is having haylage as her main forage feed, supplement it with a wafer of good clean straw as well, preferably barley straw. Don't be tempted to increase her concentrate ration.

Drinking

Your goats should drink around 1½ to 2 gallons of water a day if they are on a winter (dry) diet. Large increases over that may be worthy of investigation by your vet. Less consumption of water should not be a cause for concern so long as the water supply is both clean and fresh. Shy drinkers can be encouraged by giving them warm water. Always have your buckets raised from the ground in a bucket holder to prevent contamination of the water and always change the water at least once a day. Scrub the buckets thoroughly once a week. Adding a teaspoon of salt to the water once a day is also a good way to make sure your goat gets sufficient sodium, but if you have salt blocks in the stall this should not be necessary.

Droppings

Any sign of scour or no droppings at all need urgent attention. Scour can be dietar, but more often than not is caused by a heavy worm burden.

Scratching

Check for skin parasites and treat appropriately. Always use a magnifying glass or good reading glasses as it is easy to miss lice in particular.

AGGRESSION TO EACH OTHER

Remove the offending goat from the others or 'rescue' a persecuted goat! Assess what is causing the problem and deal with it. Overcrowding or jealousy can often result in udder biting in females and must be stopped before serious injury occurs.

COAT CONDITION

The coat should be shiny and supple. If it is dry, broken or scurfy check for parasites. If this is not the case then get a blood test done to see if the goat has a vitamin or mineral deficiency.

EYES & NOSE

These should be clear, clean and without redness. If you suspect a problem, get your vet to check them as soon as possible.

LAMENESS

Make sure feet are trimmed every six weeks and that there is no foot rot, especially between the claws.

FREE RANGE

Your goats should tick all the above boxes and be enthusiastic when you approach. Any goat that hangs back, does not rise or looks miserable needs your immediate attention.

Do this check every day and especially when routines in the household become disrupted due to visitors, celebrations etc. Remember that people have been stock watching in this way since the dawn of time. It is truly the best indicator of your animals' general health and will allow you to rest easy at night in the knowledge that all is well.

RAISING GOATS

PREVENTION AND EARLY DIAGNOSIS OF GOAT AILMENTS

With careful husbandry and good practices most common ailments can be avoided, and when they do occur they can be treated promptly by the goat keeper. Many vets have only minimal experience with goats and often an experienced goat keeper is the person to ask if you are unsure. Following or failing that, then obtaining the services of your vet must always be considered a priority and is, in fact, a legal requirement. When you contemplate goat keeping, enquiring locally about a vet with some caprine experience is worthwhile.

It should be noted that many preparations are not licensed for goat use and although sheep preparations are usually eminently suitable, care should be taken and advice sought if necessary as to which to use, particularly if the goat is producing milk for human consumption or destined for the abattoir within 72 days.

From pregnancy to birth and throughout the goat's life to its ultimate demise, I will endeavour to provide an easy reference point of common problems that can easily be dealt with by the hobby goat keeper/smallholder and when you should call for professional assistance.

CORRECTLY NAMING YOUR GOATS

DOE - A female goat of any breed. From birth to 12 months (usually documented as January of the following year in the Northern Hemisphere) it is known as a doe kid.
BUCK - a male goat of any breed which is 2 years old and over.
WETHER - a castrated male goat of any age.
GOATLING - a female goat of any breed from 12 months.
BUCKLING - An entire male goat of any breed from 12 months.
KID - a goat of any breed from birth to 12 months of age.
NORMAL TEMPERATURE OF A HEALTHY GOAT - 39-39.5°C
NORMAL HEART RATE OF A HEALTHY GOAT - 70-80 beats per minute.
NORMAL RESPIRATION RATE OF A HEALTHY GOAT - 10-30 breaths per minute
NORMAL RUMEN ACTIVITY OF A HEALTHY GOAT - 1-1.5 movements per minute.

HOW TO TAKE A TEMPERATURE - ideally this should be done rectally with a digital thermometer. If you use a glass thermometer, make sure you shake down the mercury before using it. Tie the goat up, lubricate the end of the thermometer with a little petroleum jelly, hold the goat's tail up with one hand and gently insert the thermometer. She may initially startle, but will soon relax. Record it for one minute or until the beeper sounds if using a digital with this facility.

HOW TO TAKE A HEART/PULSE RATE - you do not need a stethoscope to do this. If you place both your hands on either side of the goat's chest, behind the elbows and low down, you will be able to feel the heart rate quite clearly.

Manually checking the heart rate

HOW TO USE A STETHOSCOPE - personally, both for taking heart rates and listening to rumen activity, I prefer a stethoscope. They are easily bought for just a few pounds. You do not need a high tech one! For taking the heart rate, apply the stethoscope to the goat on the near side, just behind the elbow. Let the heart rate settle for a few seconds as it may elevate initially. Use the second hand on your watch to establish the beat. If you are monitoring a potentially unwell animal, make a physical note of the heart rate and time taken for future comparison.

RAISING GOATS

Checking rumen activity

HOW TO CHECK RESPIRATION RATE

- this is purely visual although a goat that is breathing heavily can be heard. Watch the goat's nostrils and count the in and out breath. Each breath in and out again constitutes one breath - and that is what you use to count.

HOW TO CHECK RUMEN ACTIVITY - the movement of the rumen can clearly be felt by pushing your fist firmly but gently into the goats flank which is midway between the ribs and thigh.

PREGNANCY AND BIRTH

Your goat's pregnancy will last approximately 151 days, but a variation of 4 or 5 days on either side are normal. Regardless of category type she will have been mated by a   buck or buckling anytime from July to March which is the normal cycling time for goats in the Northern Hemisphere. Most goats will be mated in the autumn with a view to a spring kidding when herbage is actively growing again. This will ensure a plentiful supply of grass for the mother and ultimately the kids who will start to graze and pick at around ten days old.

The common problems of pregnancy are:

ABORTION

This can be caused by infection or by some abnormality in the foetus. The first thing you will notice is a discharge from the goat well before her kidding date - perhaps between 30 and 140 days - and at this point you should isolate her from other goats and keep a general eye on her. If she appears to be well in herself, then it is simply a waiting game. If she seems unwell call your vet immediately. Over a period of time, which should not be more than twelve hours, she will abort the foetus and placenta. Wearing rubber gloves you should deposit the whole thing in a plastic bag for further examination to find the cause of the problem. Contact your vet so that tests can be carried out and perhaps a blood test from the doe (female/nanny). Remember that although spontaneous abortion can be non infectious, there are around 10 different serious organisms that can cause infectious abortion and these can be contracted by other goats and, in some cases, humans, so personal hygiene is absolutely essential. Whatever the outcome the goat's pen must be thoroughly cleaned and sprayed with a preparation such as Virkon S which is available from vets or agricultural merchants nationwide. Clean the goat's rear end with a mild shampoo and warm water and return her to the clean, dry and freshly bedded pen. Feed her plenty of hay and green food as available. Within a few days she will be ready to rejoin her companions and the results should be in from your vet as to what the cause was and what action is required.

CLOUDBURST

This is a false pregnancy of the goat and she, you and her body will be equally convinced that she is pregnant. She will make up gallons of amniotic fluid, probably go to term and then produce.......a lot of water! The downside is no kid, the upside is that she will probably come into milk as normal, can be mated once more and may never experience the problem again. Although considered reasonably rare, I have experienced this situation twice in one year. There is absolutely nothing you can do on this one. It is not so much an ailment as a situation and the goat will almost certainly go on to produce a healthy kid or kidss in subsequent pregnancies.

PREGNANCY TOXAEMIA

This is a metabolic disease which will require veterinary intervention and speed of recognition by the keeper is key to the goat's survival. It

RAISING GOATS

will occur generally when the goat is fed inappropriately for its stage of pregnancy. It occurs towards the end of the pregnancy, typically in the last 2 weeks. The doe's breath will have a sweet smell (pear drops) and she may grind her teeth, be off her food altogether and, worse still, become prone and reluctant to rise. This is an urgent situation and the vet must be called to administer drugs which may help to reverse the release of ketones in her blood which is causing this. At best she will deliver her kids early. Although they may or may not survive, she will recover with luck and, at worst, if left untreated, become prone. She will die within 6 or 7 days.

Toxaemia of pregnancy can be avoided by feeding plenty of good quality forage in the last 8 weeks of pregnancy and lower quantities of concentrates (typically no more than 1kg per day for a dairy goat, 500g for a fibre goat and 250g for a pygmy goat).

Daily exercise, minimising trauma and stress during the last couple of weeks of pregnancy and avoiding the mating of overweight goats should also help to reduce the likelihood of this potentially illness.

KIDDING

Approximately two weeks before the expected date of kidding the doe should be established in her kidding pen. If she is free range with access to a shelter (a must for all goats) it is possible to create a corner for her using sheep hurdles and screening them with straw bales. Clean out all old bedding and disinfect solid floors and walls. Use a preparation such as Stalosan disinfectant powder if the structure is of an organic nature.

Keep her warm and draught free and allow her out during the day if the weather allows.

Her concentrate ration should be kept low at no more than 0.5kg per day, but she should be given ad lib forage (hay/straw) which should be fed above ground, preferably in a hayrack. The importance of acclimatising her to a confined area is to allow her to build up colostral anti-bodies which will pass on to her kids and keep them safe in those first few days after birth.

KIDDING KIT

Obtain a clean, lidded bucket or a plastic box and fill it with the following essentials:

Some liquid soap and a nail brush
A pair of nail scissors
Iodine or 'purple' spray
Your vet's telephone number
Clean towel
A pair of clean waterproof over trousers
Obstetric lubricating gel
Long armed examination gloves (optional)

IMMINENT KIDDING

The signs are:

✳ A full udder (although she may have bagged up several days earlier). However full that udder is do not, under any circumstances, milk anything off. It's early contents are colostrum which is a vital first boost to the newborn kids for the first few days of life.
✳ A swollen vulva which becomes elongated and slack and a desire to stay in her pen that morning.
✳ Hollows will appear at the base of her tail and she will elevate her tail in a hooked fashion.
✳ She will circle her pen with increasing regularity and dig her bedding up, which is another good reason for a clean pen!

It is a good idea to give her plenty of clean straw while she continues with this, which could go on for several hours. Make sure she has her supply of clean hay, although she will only pick at it, if at all. Put her water bucket high enough so that she can drink it but not so low that there is any chance of her dropping a kid into it. As with humans, although there is a pattern to labour, the time the various stages take varies hugely from person to person and goat to goat, so there are no hard and fast rules as to how long this procedure will take. In my experience first staging can take from two to twelve hours so don't get too excited too early if this is

RAISING GOATS

you first birthing or you will be exhausted by the end when perhaps you might need your wits about you.

The goat will manage this stage of labour very nicely on her own and the best thing you can do is to get on with your other jobs and check on her every 30 minutes or so. You will know when things are progressing as she will have a mucous discharge and her breathing will become more rapid with a typical flare to her nostrils. If you are able, offer her some warm water to drink. This is often appreciated, but don't worry if she is not interested. Keep strangers away from her. Whilst she will appreciate her owner's quiet attention she will definitely not appreciate the next door neighbour's children or yours or other people's dogs. Remember that abnormal disturbance can protract the labour and possibly jeopardise an otherwise safe and successful kidding.

She will often lay down if she feels secure (I have never yet had one of my goats kid whilst standing) and usually gets a sort of 'far away' super concentration look and shortly after you will see her strain a couple of times at which point the water bag will appear. In first kidders this can often retract once or twice before it stays firmly outside or just within the vulva. She may 'talk' to her unborn kids by gently bleating to them in utero – she may do this for some minutes or in some case an hour or more, unfortunately you simply can't generalise on this subject. Quite quickly you will be able to see a little nose within the water bag or a nose and two hooves. If this is the case, don't worry and don't interfere; all is going 100% well! Just sit quietly and watch. Don't attempt to break the water bag membrane, the efforts of the contractions and the kid will do this perfectly well. If you break the membrane it could slow down the birth and even put the kid at risk. At least you now know that you have at least one kid arriving normally.

Get your over-trousers on now because you are going to get wet. Also make sure that your nails are as short as possible and wash your hands with the soap and scrub your nails with the nail brush. Keep the water because you may have to do this again if intervention is required with a subsequent kid. Alternatively you can use long armed examination gloves which can be purchased from any agricultural merchant. Assuming all is going well (and we'll deal with the negatives next) 2 or 3 good pushes by the doe should expel the kid into the world, at which point she may well shout as the head emerges, but don't worry, this is quite normal.

In order to give the best assistance to your goat, get down on your knees to her level and help the doe out by pulling away the membrane, especially around the kids nose and mouth. He will snort and splutter and shake his head. Now give the goat her baby to clean up and let her do it; the licking stimulates the kid into action and bonds mother and kid. While she is doing it she will hardly notice any further contractions as the next kid being born. Follow the same procedure with the next kid and then let the doe get on with the job for a while. If she has had a multiple birth, the towel can be very useful to give her a bit of a hand with the drying process, but always let her lick her kid before you come in with the towel. Her contractions will continue and after a while the placenta will appear. She will have got to her feet by now and gravity will help her expel the placenta. Under no circumstances should you pull the placenta away. She must, and will, expel this on her own. I referred to some iodine or purple spray in your kit bucket which can be used to spray the point where the umbilical cord has broken off (the cord stump), although this is not essential if your conditions are clean, but it is a wise precaution to avoid possible infection later and perhaps an unsightly umbilical hernia.

THE DIFFICULT KIDDING

I estimate, from my own statistics, that one in thirty kiddings is less than straightforward. Nevertheless, we must be mentally prepared for the worst and hopefully cope with the problems as they present themselves. It is really a question of common sense and you are a very unlucky goatkeeper if you get an insurmountable one. So what are these problems likely to be? Abnormal presentations are the most common, closely followed by the oversized kid and last come rare conditions such as Ringwomb (a failure of the cervix to dilate) and twisting or torsion of the uterus which are both thankfully uncommon, but we will touch upon them as a point of reference.

Breach births are quite common but seldom cause a problem unless the kid is very large. Sometimes one foreleg is back and you will see this quite clearly when a nose and a hoof appear with a second hoof not visible. Head back is another, somewhat more complicated situation and twins jammed at the pelvis are worse. This is where confidence and the bucket of hot water and soap come in again! Wash your hands and then re-soap them or use your long armed gloves. Soap can be substituted by lubricating gel available from any agricultural merchants. Put all your finger tips and thumb together and very gently slide your hand into the birth canal, following the line of the goats back with the back of your hand uppermost. By the time your hand is in beyond your wrist you should be able to feel what the problem is by gently rotating your hand around until you feel the retracted limb in the case of a foreleg back and a tail in the case of a breach presentation. In the case of a foreleg back gently grasp the hoof and pull it forward, keeping your hand over the hoof. This should bring almost immediate relief to the doe and the kid will be expelled very quickly. Help her out now to get the kid going. With a breach it is probably a game of patience. The kid will almost certainly be born normally but it will take a little longer. On no account should you pull a kid out, but rather wait for a contraction and ease the kid out as an aid to each contraction, pulling downward once the head and feet or rump are clearly visible

For a head back presentation, follow the same procedure but cradle the head in your hand and rotate it into position. Again a rapid resolution should follow.

In the case of twins jammed at the pelvis, the goat will have been straining for a good while with no results. Unless you have had significant experience, it is time to get assistance from an experienced goat keeper or vet. Remember that your vet may not arrive for some time and so your main job is to stay with the mother and help as much as you can. She may be shouting a lot because she will be in pain, but if you keep calm this will help her get through the situation until help arrives.

THE GENERAL RULE OF THUMB IS THAT IF YOU ARE NOT SURE WHAT YOU CAN FEEL AND THE GOAT HAS BEEN STRAINING FOR AN HOUR WITH NO RESULTS OR IS BECOMING DISTRESSED, CALL FOR HELP!

It is a sensible precaution to get your vet to check any goat that has had any kind of compromised birth which required intervention. She may need antibiotics and your vet may need to check that she has no dead kids remaining inside and that she has 'cleansed' (got rid of her placenta)

properly Never underestimate the importance of this. Far better a small vet's bill than the ramifications of dead goats and kids and the consequences and costs of disposal.

if your goat requires manual intervention at kidding she should receive 2ml of penicillin per day for five days by intramuscular injection.

POST KIDDING

If you have more than one goat keep the mother and new-borns separate from other goats for at least 24 hours. Make sure that the kids are feeding properly from the udder. They will always tend to favour one side in the first few days so check that each kid has a full tummy by feeling the abdomen. If there is an excess of colostrum on one side of the udder then utilise this by stripping some out into a sterilised bottle and freezing it for that occasion when colostrum for a weak or orphaned kid can be a lifesaver. It keeps for several years in a freezer. Very occasionally a small kid will need help to find the udder and help may be given. Once it has suckled there is not usually a further problem. I always try to make sure my kids have had a feed within two hours of birth. I avoid tubing kids unless absolutely necessary. Many veterinary manuals do recommend it but, unless you are well practised, there is a risk that the kid can inhale fluids and develop pneumonia.

The mother will benefit from some warm water and a feed of sloppy oatmeal or bran with a tablespoon of honey and a pinch of salt after kidding. Resist the temptation to give her a great big scoop of concentrates! Just make sure she has plenty of good quality hay and straw in her pen again. She will eat the afterbirth once it is dispelled and this will not hurt her, in fact it will probably give her a boost of the right sort of protein and iron. Some goat keepers will not agree with this but I have never had a problem and it is, after all, what nature intended. Failing that you are really supposed to dispose of it according to Defra rules, which means it must be incinerated. The important thing is that if the kids are born dead, malformed or the foetus is aborted before the end of the usual gestation period, then this is a much more serious matter and you should call your Animal Health Office or the Defra helpline for guidance.

RAISING GOATS

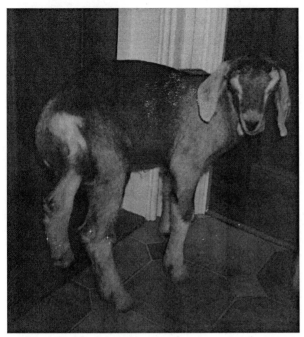

Depending on the time of year, green food is always appreciated and bananas and dates are also a luxury treat which will be readily eaten.

If you have more than one goat to kid in reasonably quick succession it is a good idea to identify the kids with a coloured spray to correspond with the same colour mark on their mother. If you don't have a coloured spray then mark the ears with a coloured felt tip marker instead.

Disbudded kid recovering from anaesthesia

When the kids are a day old check that the females have no teat abnormalities and book your vet for disbudding between four and 10 days, depending on your vet's normal practice. It is illegal in the UK to disbud kids without an anaesthetic and this too must be administered by a vet. Also check for problems with the navel. Consider the use of Enterotoxaemia vaccine (Heptavac P) at 2 weeks from unvaccinated mothers or at 12 weeks from vaccinated mothers.

POST KIDDING PROBLEMS

The most common conditions found post kidding are:

ACETONAEMIA (KETOSIS)

The symptoms of Ketosis are very similar to those of pregnancy toxaemia but the time scale is different as Ketosis is almost always a problem after delivery. It is caused by insufficient energy food in or around the fourth to sixth week of post kidding as this is when the demands on her milk are going to be the highest, particularly if she has kids at foot. The doe's breath will smell sweet (again not dissimilar to pear drops) and she will avoid eating concentrates completely. Feeding little and often is the key. If she is housed then she should be receiving the very best hay possible and/or haylage which is intended for horses (preferably a Ryegrass variety). She should be allowed this ad lib and, if the time of year permits, suitable harvested browsings. Her concentrate ration should be increased post kidding over four weeks and, if possible, fed in 3 of 4 feeds a day, but never in one go. Depending on the breed and assuming that you are using a proprietory goat mix, follow the manufacturer's feeding instructions with regard to quantities.

Although it is possible to help with the condition yourself, my advice would be to immediately call your vet who will be able to administer intravenous dextrose. This is something you cannot do yourself. The important thing is to make sure you can recognise the condition and act accordingly.

MASTITIS

Mastitis is a problem that unfortunately, once established, tends to revisit on regular occasions. It is relatively unusual for a goat rearing its own offspring and that is not milked to develop mastitis. It can be caused by bruising to the teats and udder as well as bacterial infection.

Relief can be brought to the goat initially by applying hot (but not boiling) cloths to the affected area. This can often help release the congestion and allow you to milk off the milk which is known as 'beestings.' This is because it is stringy and solid and will leave the teat in clots. Antibiotic treatment may be necessary. A goat that is known to have suffered mastitis in previous years should be managed carefully in every lactation in order to maintain usefulness as a milker. Chronic cases should be referred to your vet for anti-biotic therapy.

COMMON SKIN CONDITIONS

RINGWORM

Ringworm is a fungus that lives on wood and fences for years and is easily contracted. The goat has to have a small scratch for the fungus to enter the skin. The usual scenario is that the goat scratches on an infected post and thus introduces the fungus. It takes 10 days from introduction to signs of the first lesions. It tends to start as a small pustule that progresses to many pustules which in turn create a 'ring' of lesions which is normally the stage at which it is noticed. The goat will scratch the area(s), thus further infecting other areas of the goat house/field. Organic treatment consists of using freshly squeezed lemon juice on the site initially, followed by a dusting with Flowers of Sulphur or applying Gentian Violet. Ringworm is self-limiting and will eventually disappear on its own. However, failure to treat it will cause a major and reoccurring outbreak in all your livestock. All wooden areas where the goat has rubbed should be creosoted or sprayed with Virkon S. Keep livestock away from creosote for 2 days after application.

SKIN PARASITES

Treat goats twice a year with a topical skin application. Pour the powder or liquid down the spine from poll to tail and it will naturally follow the hair line around the goat.

If you suspect your goat has a skin problem then examine its skin closely with a magnifying glass or at the very least your very best reading glasses! Tiny droppings or eggs from lice or mites are easily missed without assistance of this kind!

MITES - are essentially mange mites or occasionally forage mites and the goat will bite and scratch at itself giving rise to a patchy, woolly appearance of the coat and latterly leathery skin patches and loss of condition in a surprisingly short time. It is important to establish which mite is causing the problem and it will be necessary for your vet to take a skin scraping for microscopic investigation in order to prescribe the correct treatment. This is an urgent situation as it is highly contagious and the goat will become debilitated very quickly.

HARVEST MITES - commonly affect grazing goats and usually inhabit the area between the claws and the lower parts of the goats' legs. They collect in clusters which show as an orangey-red dot or dots. There are literally thousands of them in each 'dot' you can see. A magnifying glass will be required to see them. The goat will bite at its lower legs and stamp its feet

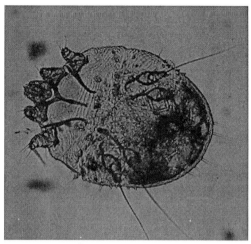

Sarcoptes mites

as they are intensely itchy. Treat with either tea tree oil, sulphur powder, or Spot On spray.

LICE - live on the coat and skin and are just visible to the naked eye but are easily spotted with a magnifying glass! Treat with louse powder such as Delete by pouring from the poll to the tail. The preparation will work its way through the coat. Treat ALL the goats, regardless of whether or not they are showing symptoms. Once treated, immediately remove them from their pens to a paddock or clean area. Remove and burn all bedding and disinfect the goat house with Virkon S. Sprinkle louse powder into all the corners and re-bed and return the goats to their house.

WORMING

Wormers fall into three different categories and it is important to identify the chemicals used in each preparation and to change your wormer annually. The importance of this is to avoid wormer resistance being established. There is a temptation to use a variety of wormers throughout the year, but this should be avoided or resistance to several wormers can be experienced.

The three groups of wormers are as follows:

RAISING GOATS

BENZAMIDAZOLES & PROBENZAMIDAZOLES - these are white coloured wormers (eg. Panacur)

LEVAMISOLE - these are yellow wormers (eg. Nilverm)

AVERMECTINES - often clear coloured (eg. Oramec)

All goats should be wormed regularly but not over wormed as this can lead to resistance to wormers and is also expensive for you. Virtually all wormers are prepared for sheep and goats metabolise drugs quicker than sheep, so you should double the sheep dose per kg when using wormers from the Benzamidazole and Lavamisole with an increase of 50% for Avermectines per kg of goat weight.

Depending on your herd size, acreage grazed and space shared with other species, your goats may need anything from a twice annual to a once every six weekly worm dosing. Advice is best sought from your vet who will know the local conditions and will be able to advise accordingly as every situation will be different. Having a worm count done once or twice a year is also a good plan. The cost is small compared to the wasteful use of wormer. You can use your veterinary practice for this or a number of direct testing laboratories can be found on the internet.

It is a good idea to worm a doe 2 days after kidding as there is often a rise of worms at this time.

ORGANIC WORMING

You may wish to avoid using chemical wormers. In this case having regular worm counts done is essential. There are various organic wormers available that usually involve dosing over a protracted period of time. One of these is Verm-X which is a pelleted wormer added to feed.

INVASIVE INJURIES

The most likely injuries that a goat is likely to sustain are from wire, broken branches, glass, biting from other goats and head injuries from other goats through butting.

Illness and Veterinary Requirements

Making sure that your grazing areas, pens and outbuildings are free from obvious hazards is your first port of call, Make sure that there are no nails sticking out, no bits of baler twine lying around, no broken glass or old (or new for that matter) farm machinery accessible to your goats. Keep thorn bushes trimmed back so that accidental injury cannot occur to eyes and noses. Should an invasive injury occur then bring the goat in and clean the area with saline solution. Use a large disposable syringe without a needle for this purpose as you can direct the jet into the wound to fully irrigate it. Use a magnifying glass to examine the wound carefully for any remaining foreign bodies and further flush the wound if required. If there is a gaping wound or a flap of skin larger than 3cm then a vet should be called to suture as necessary and administer antibiotics. Should the latter be necessary then your vet will almost certainly give you a 3 day supply of antibiotics which you can inject yourself. He/she will explain whether the antibiotics need to be administered subcutaneously (under the skin) or intra muscularly (into the muscle). Do not be afraid to ask how to do it if you are unsure.

Assuming that veterinary intervention is not required, you should then treat the irrigated wound with aloe vera gel and a topical wound powder. Aloe has wonderful healing properties and the wound powder will prevent flies attacking the site. Dab around the wound with fly repellent if flies are present, depending on the time of year. It would be wise to keep the goat penned for 2 or 3 days, dressing the wound once or twice daily. Once healing has begun keep an eye on the area for any signs of secondary infection such as pus, dying back of the skin or a bad smell. Any of these signs will necessitate a visit from a veterinarian.

BITING - female goats occasionally have a habit of attacking each others' udders with disastrous results! Usually this is caused by a group of females with kids when mis-mothering takes place or a new individual is introduced to the herd. It is something to be constantly aware of in a group of lactating females. Usually it will result only in bruising but that bruising can be a precursor to mastitis so should always be taken seriously. The offending goat needs to be removed from the herd if this is more than an isolated incident and consideration must be given as to whether re-homing of this individual is appropriate in the long term. Bruising can be dealt with by application of Udder Ointment and hot and cold compresses. Arnica cream is also a very effective treatment and would be my own first choice. Watch out for 'hot spots' developing on the udder over the next few days as this can be a sign of the early stages of mastitis.

Rips or tears of the udder tissue caused by biting are more serious and immediate veterinary intervention is mandatory if you are to keep your goat healthy and productive. A large milking udder has no chance of making a reasonable natural repair without help.

Occasionally ears get bitten or torn, the latter usually as a result of an ear tag getting entangled in wire netting or a hay feeder. Use Arnica cream in the case of bruising without broken skin and Aloe Vera for broken skin after an appropriate flushing with saline. Bruised ears can often end up alarmingly swollen but as long as there is no real heat, continued treatment with Arnica will usually resolve the problem in about a week.

BUTTING - this is something that can happen at any time. Avoid keeping horned and hornless goats together as the horned goats are at a distinct advantage and can inflict some lethal injuries. Young males will often play fight and this is fine unless it is continued and prolonged. If you see anything that causes bleeding or that you can see is becoming serious, then separate the offending individuals. Treat horn bud injuries with anti-septic spray or wound powder and keep the injured goat away from other animals until healing is underway and be very careful about fly strike on the wounded areas. Use your intelligence to work out why the problem occurred and address the management of your stock accordingly.

LAMENESS - establish which foot your goat is actually lame on. It will 'drop' on the good foot and 'go light' on the bad one. A goat with a shuf-fley gait is probably lame on all four feet and this is likely to be caused by laminitis due to overfeeding or scald, a bacterium which thrives in grassland in temperatures consistently over 10°C and as such is very much a spring complaint.

Secure the goat and check the affected foot. Does it need trimming? Is the foot damaged, sore or bleeding? Is there anything stuck between the digits or soreness in the lower leg? Is there any swelling or heat? Having established which one of these things it could be, take the necessary remedial action for invasive injuries, skin parasites, footrot or laminitis (see below) or trim the hooves as necessary.

FOOTROT AND LAMINITIS - footrot is a condition caused by a bacterium and needs temperatures consistently above 10°C to proliferate. The goat has heat and swelling between the claws of the front feet and in white hoofed goats a redness will be seen around the coronet. The hoof becomes underun quite quickly and there can be separation of the horn from the sensitive laminae. As a result the goat is extremely lame and will often graze on its knees. It is mainly a condition of outdoor goats but can be contracted by housed goats and passed on throughout the herd. It can be controlled in fields by removing the goats from the pasture for a minimum of ten days and returning them after that period of time has elapsed and the feet have been treated. Do this by dipping the feet in zinc sulphate. If this is for just a few goats it can be done by immersing the feet individually into the solution in a plastic tub or small bucket. Where there are a lot of goats a foot bath should be used. Where it is a serious ongoing problem the goats can be vaccinated with a vaccine called Foot-vax. It is intended for sheep but most vets will supply it for goats.

Laminitis is the inflammation of the laminae of the goat's feet. The laminae are like little leaves of horn which overlay one another. If the goat has access to sudden high levels of protein which can be through either concentrated feed or lush spring grass, this can cause these 'leaves' to become inflamed and engorged with blood which makes the goat extremely lame and the feet hot and painful to the touch. The goat will lie down or stand with its weight on its heels. Addressing the diet and obtaining anti-inflammatory drugs from your vet are the required course of action. Once the goat recovers it will have a tendency to contract laminitis again so great attention to diet must be employed.

Laminitis can also be a complication of post kidding illnesses such as mastitis and metritis.

HOOF TRIMMING - a vital part of goat husbandry which should be undertaken every six weeks. It is particularly important in the assistance to recovery and avoidance of hoof conditions such as footrot and laminitis.

Use a hoof knife and/or hoof shears to trim correctly and follow with a 'surfoam' file or coarse sandpaper. Take small slices off at a time to avoid over trimming which can cause the hoof to bleed. If this should happen the goat will be lame for a few days, but you must treat the hoof with antibiotic spray or tea tree oil for several days to avoid infection entering the wound.

Correct trimming of the foot

INAPPETANCE - Goats can lose their appetite for a number of reasons and need watching for signs and symptoms of illness, poisoning and disease as a result. It is vital that they recommence eating as soon as possible as rumen activity is vital for their survival. Initially check that food is not contaminated by the goat, other goats or other animals. Check that it has a clean water supply. Take the goat's temperature and other vital signs. Check whether it has diarrhoea. If these are all normal try offering a 'favourite food' or treats such as digestive biscuits, grapes, banana, apple or willow. Occasionally a few ivy leaves or a piece of honeysuckle will restore a goat's appetite. Having exhausted all possibilities, if the goat has not begun to eat after four hours your vet should be consulted.

A goat on the verge of labour will often not eat for 3 or 4 hours beforehand. Providing that all is progressing normally you can re-introduce light feeding after delivery

DIARRHOEA - sudden changes in diet, poisoning, chronic worm infestation and toxin producing bacteria can all cause this problem. Avoid sudden feeding changes including giving gluts of vegetables from your holding. Worm your goats regularly (see WORMING) and give strict attention to cleanliness of feeding utensils and housing. Do not graze kids on land that was grazed by last year's kids as there may be a risk of Coccidiosis. Any diarrhoea that does not clear up in 24 hours should be considered an urgent veterinary problem. Your vet will undoubtedly take a sample for laboratory investigation and the goat/s can be treated with anthelmintics (wormers), antibiotics or the appropriate medication as necessary. Vaccination with Heptavac P Plus will avoid the risk of clostridial diseases which can quickly kill goats(see vaccination).

Treat dietary diarrhoea (scour) by increasing hay and decreasing concentrates. Oak leaves, although on my poisons list, do have a binding action so can be fed in small quantities. The goat should be given a proprietory electrolyte such as Lectlade (see veterinary kit list) according to the manufacturer's instructions or, failing that, a dessertspoonful of glucose and a teaspoonful of salt in approximately half a gallon of water and given in a bucket (do not drench!). Kaolin can also be used, but consult with your vet on quantity and severity of the scour. If more than one of your goats has scour this must be investigated by your vet as soon as possible.

DIETARY DEFICIENCIES

Dietary deficiencies can manifest themselves in many ways but usually poor coat condition, low milk production and failure to breed efficiently are obvious signs. By feeding your goats a good and balanced diet and using a proprietary goat mix, most problems are avoidable. Do not use feed which has been prepared for other species, particularly sheep. Sheep feed does not contain copper and goats do need copper. As standard your goats should have access to a caprine salt/mineral lick and, if possible, a good vitamin/mineral supplement such as Caprivite. Check with your local vet what deficiencies your local soil may have and take advice as to how to correct these. As a general rule the UK is deficient in both selenium and cobalt and so a combination of hanging a 'Rockie Red' block which has added copper and a 'Rockie SC Sheep' block will provide both selenium and cobalt. Any goat showing signs of unthriftiness should be blood tested by your vet to eliminate any serious notifiable problems such as Caprine Arthritis Encephalitis(CAE), TB (which was identified in goats in the UK for the first time in many years in 2008), Scrapie and Johnne's Disease.

Fibre goats (Angora, Cashmere/Cashgora) need to have a higher protein level in their diets than other goats. They need to be fed the same as a lactating dairy doe as the growth of fleece takes large proportions of the goat's energy. As a result, if the dietary requirements are not met, the quality of the fleece will be lower and the goat's bodily condition will suffer. It is important to condition score a fibre goat by feeling its hindquarters for fleshiness as the coat will hide the skeletal condition. If not you may have a shock when the goat is shorn. Additional sulphur is also required by fibre goats and this can be achieved by feeding one ounce of Sulphur Sublimed per animal per week, mixed through the weekly ration. Sulphur Sublimed, also known as Flowers of Sulphur, is an acrid yellow powder. If it is any other colour you have the wrong kind of sulphur so don't use it! Alternatively you can supplement the diet with an Angora specific supplement such as Caprivite Angora.

POISONING - unlike most livestock goats seem to have a knack of finding all the food that poisons them! Great care must be taken when collecting browsings or turning a goat out onto pasture that there is nothing growing in hedges and on stone walls that might poison them. Certain plants will poison a goat quickly and create a problem from which it is unlikely to recover. Generally speaking, if a goat has a full rumen, ingestion of small quantities of poisonous plants have a lesser effect but plant poisoning in goats is totally avoidable if you are observant and careful of your goat grazing areas. Always check the perimeters and hedgerows and if your holding or field is flanked by neighbours, pay them a friendly visit and request that they do not feed your animals in any circumstances or deposit their garden debris on your boundaries.

Should your goat be unfortunate enough to ingest a poisonous plant or substance this is an emergency situation. Try your utmost to determine the cause of the poisoning and call your vet immediately.

PLANTS POISONOUS TO ALL RUMINANTS BY INGESTION

A   ACONITE
        ACORNS
        AFRICAN VIOLET
        ASTER
        ALDER BUCKTHORN
        AZALE

B   BLACK BRYONY
        BLACK NIGHTSHADE
        BLUEBELL
        BOX
        BRACKEN
        BROOM
        BUKTHORN
        BULBS(ALL PARTS OFALL GARDEN VARIETIES)
        BUTTERCUP

C   CASTOR OIL PLANT
        CELANDINE
        CHARLOCK
        CHERRY LAUREL
        CHICKWEED
        CHRYSANTHEMUM
        CLOVER(RED)
        COLUMBINE
        COMFREY
        CORN COCKLE
        COWBANE
        CUCKOO PINT(LORDS & LADIES)
D   DARNEL
        DEADLY NIGHTSHADE
        DELPHINIUM
        DOGBANE

RAISING GOATS

E   ELDERBERRY

F   FOXGLOVE
        FUME WORT

G   GOAT WEED
        GRASS CUTTINGS
        GROUND IVY
        GROUNDSEL
        GUNNERA

H   HELLEBORE
        HEMLOCK
        HEMLOCK WATER DROPWORT
        HEMP NETTLE
        HENBANE
        HERB PARIS
        HONEYSUCKLE
        HORSE CHESTNUT
        HORSE RADISH
        HYPERICUM
        HYDRANGEA

I   INDIAN HEMP
        IRIS
        IVY

K   KALE (IN EXCESS)

L   LABURNHAM
        LARKSPUR
        LAUREL
        LILY OF THE VALLEY
        LINSEED

LLEYLANDII
LOBELIA
LUPIN

M   MARSH MARIGOLD
MEADOW SAFFRON
MELILOT
MERCURY
MILKWEED
MONK'S HOOD

O   OAK
OLEANDER
ORCHID

P   PEACH
PIMPERNEL
PERIWINKLE
POPPY
POTATO (AERIAL PARTS AND GREEN POTATOES)
PLUM
PRIVET
R   RAGWORT
RAPE
RHEUM
RHUBARB
RHODEDENDRON
RUSH

S   SPINDLEBERRY
ST. JOHN'S WORT
SOAP WORT
SORREL
SPRUCE FAMILY
SPURGE

SUDAN GRASS (GREEN SHOOTS)
SUGAR BEET TOPS - (OK FOR SHEEP)
SWISS CHEESE PLANT

T THORN APPLE
TOMATO (GREEN PARTS)

W WHITE BRYONY
WOODY NIGHTSHADE
WOLF'S BANE

Y YELLOW RATTLE
YEW

NB. Many of these plants have low toxicity and many will not be eaten unless the animal is extremely hungry, but some are fatal or the consequences of ingestion irreversible.

ROUTINE VACCINATION AND ADMINISTRATION

Vaccination of goats is not considered essential by some, but my personal feelings are that it is truly essential!

BLUETONGUE - the use of Bluetongue vaccine (currently BTV8) is not yet compulsory in the UK, but I suspect it may become so. This vaccine can only be obtained from a vet for your own administration. Goats should receive 2 subcutaneous injections of 1ml given 4 weeks apart, followed by six monthly boosters. Kids can be vaccinated at four weeks old for the vaccine produced by Intervet and at 3 months old for vaccine produced by Merriel. Bottles of vaccine must be used within eight hours of opening and contain a minimum of 20 doses so, for small scale keeping, obtaining syringes of vaccine from your vet if you only have two or three goats to vaccinate makes economic sense. (Of course if you have cows or sheep as well you could use a full bottle on each occasion). Your vet will usually time the opening of a bottle with the needs of several other small scale keepers and so it will be necessary to speak to the surgery in advance. Once on the list most practices will contact you just prior to your vaccine requirement to find out how many doses you require. The cost will be around £1 per dose which is a small price to pay to protect both yours and the wider National Flock. Smallholders often get blamed for the spread of disease so we should be especially vigilant that we get it right! Bluetongue is a very real and potentially catastrophic disease.

TETANUS AND CLOSTRIDIAL VACCINE - tetanus is vital (for you too, but go to your Doctor!) and goats should be vaccinated every six months by using Heptavac P Plus vaccine which covers tetanus and all the clostridial diseases, some of which are transmissible to man so really should not be ignored.

This vaccine should be given as a primary course of two injections given 4 to 6 weeks apart. Give 2ml subcutaneously to each goat with a six monthly 2ml booster. It can be given to kids from 2 weeks old, but if the pregnant doe has received a booster 2 to 4 weeks before she has kidded, then vaccination of the kids can be deferred until 10 weeks of age. Vaccinate all kids, even if they are destined for the freezer.

REMEMBER THAT NO VACCINES SHOULD BE GIVEN CLOSER THAN 2 WEEKS APART SO YOU WILL NEED TO WORK OUT A REGIME TO MAKE SURE THAT YOUR BOOSTERS FALL INTO THE RIGHT TIME OF THE YEAR AND THAT THEY DON'T CLASH WITH THE BLUETONGUE VACCINATION WHICH NEEDS TO BE DONE IDEALLY IN FEBRUARY AND AUGUST TO COINCIDE WITH THE RISE OF MOSQUITOES AND MIDGES!

HOW TO KEEP IT CLEAN - the importance of keeping an opened bottle of vaccine hygienic throughout the vaccination process cannot be emphasised enough. Abscesses can form very easily on a goat through bad hygiene which can lead to pain, infection and spoilage of the goat's appearance or skin if it is destined for meat or skin production.

Use one needle for the withdrawal of vaccine from the bottle. Leave it in situ and attach the syringe to a new needle. Use a new needle for every goat. You can use the withdrawal needle for the last goat you vaccinate.

RAISING GOATS

A SUBCUTANEOUS injection means beneath the skin. The best way to ensure that the vaccine goes below the skin and not into a muscle or blood vessel is to take a pinch of skin (like a tent) and push the needle into it, making sure that the needle does not reappear out the other side! Using a needle of the correct length is also important and

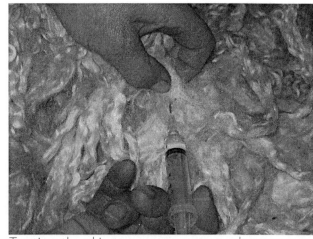

Tenting the skin to ensure correct subcutaneous injection.

I would suggest ¾″ for adult goats and ½″ for kids. If you feel more comfortable cleaning the area with surgical spirit first then by all means do so, but if your goats are clean, kept in clean conditions and you use a separate needle for each animal, this won't really be necessary.

Intramuscular injection site

AN INTRAMUSCULAR injection means into the muscle. A large muscle mass needs to be chosen, either in the hindquarters or the shoulder. With someone holding the goat, if possible, or, if not, after tying it up, gently but firmly 'prime' the area with the heel of your clenched fist.

ARTHRITIS

Arthritis in goats can take any one of four possible forms. As a goat keeper I have experienced three of the four forms but thankfully not the very worst. I will try to explain the various forms and their prevention and treatment in descending order!

NON-SEPTIC ARTHRITIS - this is a temporary and relatively minor problem usually associated with damage to a limb or joint. The classic scenario would be that the healthy, happy goat goes out to graze and comes in again feeling and looking perfectly well to her owner's eye. The following morning she has a swollen joint (or two) as a result of a twist or sprain in the field or perhaps, in the case of a stall fed goat, from catching a leg/hoof in a rack or rail within the stall. She will normally be happy and bright and feed as normal.

The best course of action is to support the joint with an elastic bandage (not too tight!) if she will tolerate it and rest. The application of Arnica cream will also aid recovery by reducing bruising, heat and soothing any pain. Recovery should only take a few days, when careful exercise can be resumed.

DJD-DEGENERATIVE JOINT DISEASE - exactly what the name implies and with a number of causative factors. An ageing goat is likely to develop this problem. As with her human counterparts a genetic inheritance factor is at play here and general wear and tear on joints over many years will precipitate this problem. Many goats live well into their teens today and we owe it to them not to allow the pain of severe arthritis to linger. We can help by adding cider vinegar to their feed, but not so much as to imbalance the complexities of the goat's digestive processes. A tablespoonful a day should be enough. A potassium/codliver oil based vitamin supplement can also be helpful. I have found the horse supplement Codlivine a helpful additive in this respect. Approximately a quarter of the equine dose will suffice. If the goat is not a milking animal or a buck, consider the feed you are using. Is it too high in calcium? Too much calcium in the diet can be a pre-cursor to DJD. Bucks need far less calcium in their diet than lactating females and yet most commercial goat feeds are aimed at the dairy goat, not the entire male, wether or dry female. If your goat is a pet or a working or wethered male, consider mixing your own feed with a lower calcium content.

SEPTIC ARTHRITIS - a much more startling ailment and one which, in my own experience, has led me to take preventative action for future reference. With septic arthritis the swellings are both startling and dramatic and follow a generalised infection or bacteraemia, otherwise known as blood poisoning. Often this can occur unnoticed at birth when infection can enter the navel. The organisms 'settle' within the goat's joints, causing degenerative changes and latterly severe pain. At some point later, the goat becomes extremely ill and the joints swell, leading to so much pain that the goat lies down most of the time, her digestion suffers and eventually a total breakdown of her metabolism occurs and she will die. It is better, at this hopeless state of affairs, to humanely destroy the goat to save her prolonged suffering. Just such a case happened to me last year when a lovely dairy goat I had bought arrived with a small but healing tear in her udder. She recovered well only to then succumb to the infection some three months later when her resources were lowered which we could only relate to the stress of joining a large herd. Antibiotic injections failed to improve things as the infection was too far established and humane destruction was the only option. If she had received antibiotic injections at the time of injury, she would probably be alive today. My recommendation would be to always dress the naval of the newborn with iodine and always give a course of antibiotics after any invasive injury. Probably the worst worry of finding these symptoms in a 'bought in' goat is the fear that maybe this goat has brought in the worst of the arthritic diseases in goats, CAE. Have your herd/goat(s) regularly tested for this disease. Although rare in the UK, there are still symptomless carriers around and when buying a goat you should always seek proof of a recent CAE test on the whole herd.

CAPRINE ARTHRITIS ENCEPHALITIS (CAE) - This disease will affect many joints. It is a 'retrovirus.' a viral infection of mature goats and has a long incubation period of several years. The knees are almost always affected and often the fetlocks, hips and stifle joints. Initially it can be mistaken for any of the other forms of arthritis but in a milking goat it will have crept up on you for a season or so. You will notice a year on year drop in the milk yield and the udder may become hardened in places. Her kids may also show signs of the encephalitis part of the disease by displaying nervous symptoms, difficulty in standing and a twisting of the head. They 'go down' and may 'paddle' with their front legs. A goat may have the disease for some time before she shows any symptoms which can often be triggered by stress such as kidding, moving herds etc.

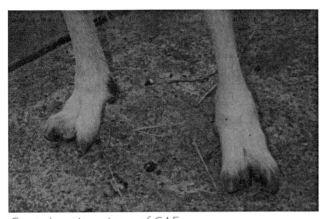

Goat showing signs of CAE

It is spread by nasal secretions and is passed from mother to kid in colostrum and saliva or nasal secretions. It is also probably passed by blood contact, the most likely being 'shared needles' during vaccination (never a good idea for the few pence saving). Ask your vet about ELISA testing to detect infected animals. Details can also be found on the British Goat Society website.

WHEN THE END IS INEVITABLE....AND THE LAW

The worst decision that any livestock keeper has to make is to take a life. Some of your goats maybe be destined for the freezer and so that mindset is already established and is easier to deal with, but sometimes we have to make decisions of another kind because a goat is very sick, very old or unthrifty, As humans we have the ability to end the suffering of animals and must realise that whatever our thought processes are, animals do not understand them and nor do they understand the concept of being killed. If we are very ill or in pain we know that in the passage of time things will change. An animal does not know that. For all animals, suffering is the here and the now and is something they must endure until it becomes unendurable. We can change that and must recognise when that is the case.

Goats going to an abattoir for human consumption has been explored in Chapter 5. If you cannot bear the thought of your unwanted goat kids entering the food chain either for your own consumption or that of others, then have unwanted kids put down at birth by humane injection by your vet. Alternatively, you can rear them kindly and with compassion

RAISING GOATS

and go with them to a small local abattoir, if possible, having prearranged the visit to be at a 'quiet' time so that they can be quickly despatched and you can see the carcasses before you leave or, in some cases, you will be allowed to watch the process if you so wish. This way you will satisfy yourself that all was done well and humanely. Never sell your kids to someone for meat unless you are personally acquainted with them and know their methods and facilities. How often have I heard, "Oh, they went to the man that takes all the unwanted kids." You might be lucky but your goats may end up as the victims of ritual slaughter or worse.

Goats that have reached the end of their 'working' lives and cannot be kept as companion animals, who are old and unthrifty or are terminally sick, should be humanely despatched by your vet by lethal injection if possible. Your local knacker man is also a possibility. Make sure you have the contact details them in a safe place or on your mobile phone for emergencies. These people are expert in what they do and they do an awful lot and it is quick and skilled as the goat is shot through the head and literally drops where it stands. The advantage of the knacker man is that they will take the carcass away. If the goat is put down by a vet by shooting with a captive bolt or lethal injection you will have to deal with the disposal which will mean a collection for incineration or delivery of the dead goats by yourself to the nearest animal crematorium. The costs of this vary but can range from thirty to a hundred pounds.

A GOAT, REGARDLESS OF ITS STATUS, EVEN IF IT IS A PET OR A PYGMY, IS AN AGRICULTURAL ANIMAL AND MUST BE DISPOSED OF CORRECTLY AND LEGALLY. YOU CANNOT, UNDER ANY CIRCUMSTANCES, BURY IT ON YOUR OWN LAND, ALTHOUGH YOU MAY LEGALLY BURY THE CREMATED REMAINS.

Inevitably, if you are a stock keeper, then sooner or later you are going to be faced with these problems, so having a contingency plan in advance and sticking to it are an essential veterinary part of compassionate small scale farming.

ORGANIC OR OTHERWISE?

In a bid to be organic or, shall we say chemical free, there are a number of homeopathic options for caring for your goats. My essential first aid kit for goat keepers encompasses many organic remedies but if you want or need to be totally purist for personal or legal reasons, for instance if you are organically registered, then taking advice from your Organic Status Provider is essential and you should perhaps enlist the services of a homeopathic vet.

A list of homeopathic vets can be found by going to www.bahvs.com or by phoning 07768 322075. A list of conventional veterinary practices can be obtained by going to www.rcvs.org.uk

ESSENTIAL FIRST AID AND VETERINARY KIT FOR ALL GOAT KEEPERS

Thermometer
Stethoscope
Hand washing gel/alcohol
Several pairs of well fitting disposable rubber gloves
Povodine iodine concentrate
Saline solution (homemade is fine in a sterilised container)
Lubricating gel/Petroleum jelly
Virkon S sachets (for disinfecting stalls and utensils)
Syringes (disposable or re-useable)
Needles: ½˝ (for kids) and ¾˝ (for adults)
An empty sterilised washing up liquid bottle and an 8˝ silicone tube to fit the nozzle for drenching
A large disposable syringe for wound dressing
Ditto for wormer
Magnifying glass
Aloe Vera gel or spray
Arnica cream
Wound powder (something suitable for horses is fine)
Lectlade Electrolyte solution or powder
Organic anti-parasitic powder such as 'Delete' or a chemical spray or

RAISING GOATS

pour-on such as Spot-On
Fly spray
Mint udder cream
BTV8 vaccine - must be used or disposed of within 8 hours of opening and refrigerated before opening. Best obtained by the syringe from your vet if you only have a few animals to vaccinate
Heptavac P vaccine (observe storage guidance)
Penicillin from your vet for assisted birth kidding (as above)
Wormer type (see worming)
Sharp round ended scissors
Garden sprayer for economic disinfection of pens, utensils and surrounding woodwork - kept specifically for the purpose
A clean lidded bucket for veterinary use only

ISOLATION AND QUARANTINE

If it becomes necessary to isolate a goat for the safety of other animals, try to put the goat within eye and ear shot of other goats as they can become more distressed by being taken away from their companions.

When purchasing new stock, keeping them quarantined for 10 days is a good idea. It also gives existing goats time to become familiar with the sight of them. Make sure there is no nose to nose contact or sharing of air space, so a shed or pen within eye and ear shot of existing goats is ideal, but where physical contact between them is not possible. Wear rubber gloves when working with the new goats and remove them before attending to your existing ones. Do not share drinking or feeding vessels. This may seem a little extreme but it will be well worth it if your new acquisitions show signs of disease during the days they are quarantined, which can turn into a very expensive problem if you have a lot of goats.

Utilise the time in quarantine to worm and start a vaccination programme. Only accept that the goat has been vaccinated if you have seen documentary evidence of this.

20 WAYS TO AVOID ACCIDENTS, INJURY AND DISEASE

1 Feed ad lib high fibre forage at all times i.e. hay and haylage, BUT NOT silage and use the best quality feed, forage and bedding that you can.

2 Check for poisonous plants, trees and shrubs wherever the goats have access.

3 Avoid sudden changes of diet or increases in certain parts of it just because you may have a glut of certain foods on your holding.

4 Worm and vaccinate regularly and keep accurate records of this: both are a legal and essential husbandry requirement.

5 Treat for skin parasites at least twice a year, depending on your choice of preparation.

6 Creosote fence posts and gates to avoid fungal spores remaining on them.

7 Thoroughly disinfect all pens, hurdles, drinking vessels and feed buckets, walls and floors at least once a year with Virkon S in a garden sprayer, having thoroughly cleaned out and swept the accommodation first. Allow to dry and re-bed before allowing the goats back in.

8 Trim hooves every six weeks.

9 Change drinking water twice daily and scrub troughs and drinkers weekly.

10 Always feed and milk goats at the same times each day.

11 Always disinfect pens when changing goats over.

12 Quarantine new animals for 10 days.

13 Never kid a goat in a pen where other goats have kidded previously without thorough cleansing.

14 Do not turn out kids on an area where the previous years kids or lambs have grazed to avoid coccidiosis infection.

15 Check your goats at least twice daily.

16 Always keep more than one goat. A single goat is a vulnerable one and more likely to succumb to disease than those kept with companions.

17 Be cautious about leaving collars on your goats, particularly if they are free range. Because of their browsing techniques it can be very easy for a goat to become entangled in branches and strangle itself. If required sheep collars, which are wide and close fitting, can be employed. They will break with tension whereas a webbing or leather collar is less likely to do so.

RAISING GOATS

18 Never tether a goat, however 'hi-tech' you think your methods are! At one time the tethering of goats was almost the norm in the UK but deaths through strangulation, broken limbs, hunger and thirst have proved that this is a totally unacceptable option and in certain circumstances can actually be illegal.

19 ALWAYS accurately complete your Animal Medicine Record Book after each and every treatment, identifying the goats by name and number. It is an essential point of referral and is also required by Law.

20 Avoid stress in handling, penning or moving goats. **In the UK it is a criminal offence not to deal with sick livestock in a timely and appropriate manner, summoning professional help if required.**

GOOD NURSING - THE KEY TO RECOVERY

ALWAYS REMEMBER: Your own good nursing of the sick or compromised animal is probably the most important thing you will ever do for your goat. You will know that it is a sensitive, intelligent creature that entrusts itself to its keeper. Moral support, determination and constant attention can sometimes be the difference between life and death. Talk constantly and quietly to your ailing/recovering goat and leave a radio on quietly playing classical music if possible. Leave a safe nightlight on during darkness. Offer tepid water with a teaspoonful of salt to every 5 litres to encourage drinking. Pick grass and other foliage and offer it regularly to the goat. Remove anything that is not eaten after 12 hours. Young dock leaves are often enjoyed as are willow twigs and leaves.

IN SUMMARY: Never be frightened to summon help if in any doubt about your own diagnosis of a problem. The loss and financial consequences of disposal and re-stocking will be far greater than the vet's bill, personal loss and self-recrimination.

Chapter 8

ZOONOSES AND THE SMALLHOLDER

We love our animals but we must never forget that they can be a source of infection for us, our families and those who do not come into contact with livestock every day.

Most people who live with livestock have a pretty good immunity to many things connected to them but there are a number of ailments that are transmissible to man and are of varying significance to our health. As with all things knowledge is the key to safety and survival and in this Chapter I shall try to guide you through the conditions that breach the species barrier and can be contracted by humans. These conditions are known as ZOONOSES.

WHO, WHY AND WHEN?

❋ Who? Virtually all animals, both domestic and agricultural, carry a risk to the health of humans.. The elderly, those with underlying illness or a compromised immune system, the very young and visitors to farms and smallholdings are at the greatest risk.

❋ Why? Sometimes poor hygiene both in animals and humans can be a causative factor and sometimes it's just bad luck.

❋ When? If an animal is ill in itself, has a skin problem or during the birthing process and directly afterwards during the post partum period.

ZOONOSES AND THE LAW

Truly serious diseases such as Anthrax, Brucellosis, Bovine TB and BSE are both reportable and notifiable diseases which have received much publicity and need no introduction here. There are, of course, more notifiable diseases than these but these are the ones that affect and kill humans in true or variant forms.

RAISING GOATS

Effectively, all zoonoses are caused by micro-organisms which are subject to what we know as COSHH. This is the Control of Substances Hazardous to Health. It requires that all employers and indeed self-employed people to do the following:

⁂ Assess the risks to health from work activities.

⁂ Prevent, or where this is not reasonably practical, adequately control exposure to the hazardous substance.

⁂ Introduce control measures.

⁂ Inform, instruct and train employees about the risks and precautions taken to avoid those risks.

⁂ Regularly review risk assessments and the effectiveness of the control measures in place.

Now this might seem like a load of red tape and you may say - well, I don't employ anyone, this is a hobby and I'm not self-employed - but let your mind run on a bit and apply these regulations to yourself and your family and friends and you will get my meaning. It is really quite surprising what you find out about your holding and the livestock on it when you start to take a deeper look.

CHILDREN AND PREGNANT WOMEN

So long as children are taught to wash their hands after handling animals, especially young animals where the risks of tummy upsets such as Salmonella are greatest, and poultry too, then the risks are immediately reduced. Proper hand washing is the very best thing that anyone can do to avoid infection of any kind and also wearing an overall for animal husbandry work (the children too!).

If hand washing facilities are not easy to access outside, then using an alcohol gel is also effective. Make sure your children don't put their hands in their mouths while working around animals.

If you are pregnant you may risk miscarriage if you are infected with CHLAMYDIA which can cause enzootic abortion in sheep and goats. It is therefore unwise for anyone expecting a baby to be involved with the lambing or kidding process.

People who have had an organ transplant or do not have a spleen are also at a higher risk from zoonoses.

HOW TO STAY SAFE AROUND THE HOLDING

! Make sure that all your tools and equipment are in good order and therefore less likely to allow you to become injured by them, causing cuts and abrasions that can subsequently become infected.

! Use syringes and needles with great care and if you take blood samples, use vacuum tubes rather than a syringe.,(This will not affect most goat keepers as virtually all blood samples, if required, will be taken by your vet as a legal requirement). Always have a Sharps box to dispose of spent needles.

! Never use mouth to mouth resuscitation on newborn animals. Use the usual methods such as massaging the new born or tickling its nose with straw and clearing its airways manually and gently swinging it from side to side by the hind legs.

! Avoid handling afterbirths and birth fluids with bare hands and always burn or bury them.

! Control rats and mice and always pick them up with a shovel or fork or gloved hands.

! Wear protective clothing when birthing animals.

! Use face protection to avoid splashes from urine or placental fluids.

! Wash any cuts or grazes immediately with soap and running

water as an absolute minimum precaution.

!   Cover wounds (preferably with a waterproof dressing or wear a latex or rubber glove on top of a non waterproof dressing if it is on your hands) while working with animals or around the holding. Remove wet dressings as soon as you are indoors and allow the air to get to them while you are in a clean area before re-dressing as required.

!   Wash not just your hands but your arms as well, removing watches and rings in the process (beneath watch straps is often where the first signs of fungal infections, such as Ringworm, occur) when you have finished working with your animals or cleaning pens and barns.

So that's the avoidance procedures taken care of! But WHAT exactly are we avoiding?

The top zoonoses for us all to be aware of are:

BOVINE TB

A disease which is frequently in the news is Bovine Tuberculosis. The spread of it is often blamed on badgers, but deer are probably just as guilty. Whatever and however it is spread, it is sadly a disease that is here to stay for a long time and so again we, as smallholders, must take care to avoid infection to ourselves.

Infection is caused by inhalation of infected spray from the noses of cattle, hand to mouth infection from mucous from the respiratory tract of infected animals and not following the basic hygiene rules of our old ally, hand washing!

People who have had the BCG immunisation in childhood will have some, though not complete protection from this disease. Unfortunately, this immunisation is no longer given to children in schools and although you can ask your GP for a vaccination, unless a group of 20 or more people are having it done, it cannot be offered. Those at the highest risk from this infection, ie those who live and work on farms with known infection, should persist in their attempts to get this vaccination for themselves.

If you suspect that any of your cattle may have TB you must report it to the Animal Health Office.

Cattle affected will have coughing bouts, a rattling in the throat similar to a snoring sound, loss of weight and lumps in the udder. However, this list is not exhaustive and cattle with the condition may not yet be displaying these problems and so regular testing is vital.

Never buy cattle that have not been tested for TB.

BSE (BOVINE SPONGIFORM ENCEPHALOPATHY) AND THE HUMAN VARIANT, VCJD (CREUTZFELDT JACOB DISEASE)

This complex disease and its variant is thought to be transmissible only by food. There is no evidence that it is contracted by exposure to infected animals or by those working with the carcasses of infected animals. With the food chain controls we have in the UK the risks are low and the only responsibility we have is to report to the Animal Health Office any animal which displays nervous symptoms which could be attributable to this condition

CRYPTOSPORIDIOSIS

This is a disease which can cause similar symptoms to Ecoli but also involves flu like symptoms that can last for several weeks. The very young and the elderly are particularly vulnerable to this disease. It is caused by a protozoa and is carried by calves, lambs, deer and goats. Transmission to humans is caused by contact with animal dung and water that has been contaminated by animal droppings.

It is sensible to assume that ALL your animals of these species are carrying this disease and also Ecoli O157 and therefore not take risks with hygiene and, in particular, hand washing. Visitors to your holding are more vulnerable than you are, so try to be responsible by insisting

RAISING GOATS

they wash their hands before leaving your set up.

If you have a holding that receives regular visitors for whatever reason it is wise to put up signs to ask people to wash their hands. If your holding has Local Authority consents for visitors then your EHO (Environmental Health Officer) will walk you through the requirements.

ECOLI (ESCHERICHIA COLI 0157)

This is a name that we are all familiar with, but do we know what it is? It is a bacterium that lives in the gut of animals including cattle, sheep, goats and deer, as well as pets and wild birds. The animal carriers of Ecoli will experience no ill effects, but when humans are infected with it the toxins it produces cause a range of illnesses from diarrhoea to kidney failure and it can be fatal.

In humans very few Ecoli organisms are needed to cause acute infection. These can be caught by handling dung or coming into contact with dung which is inevitable when working with or even grooming animals.

This problem can be totally avoided by rigorous hand washing before eating or putting your hands in your mouth. This is particularly important with children, of course.

Any overalls which are used on the farm should be washed after use and not brought into the household. The same applies to anyone preparing food for themselves or a family if they are wearing clothes that have been worn on the farm or holding for work with or around animals.

PSITTACOSIS

The bird illness! It is caused by an organism known as Chlamydia psittaci and is carried by most birds including turkey, ducks, chickens, bantams, geese, guinea fowl, quail, peafowl, guinea fowl and wild birds, caged birds and exotics. So no hiding place really.

Humans that contract this disease suffer flu like symptoms which can develop into pneumonia and occasionally become endocarditic, which is an inflammation of the heart. It can also cause hepatitis and death.

Infected birds shed the disease in dust and droppings and nasal discharge. This is usually contracted in humans by inhalation of the same. Avoid sweeping out the dry droppings of birds, but if you do, wear a respirator style face mask with a protection factor of at least 20.

If good animal husbandry practises are employed and birds that are unwell are isolated and tested, this condition can be controlled and avoided.

Q FEVER

This disease is mostly carried by cattle and sheep, although there have been cases in France from goats. It causes flu like symptoms in humans with muscle cramps, headache and extreme tiredness. Sometimes secondary infections occur such as pneumonia and liver and heart valve damage.

Infection is caused by inhalation of dust that has been contaminated with birth product, dung or urine. It can survive for many years in an environment if given suitable conditions, but by keeping your animals' pens scrupulously clean and thoroughly cleaning after each birth, then this disease can be avoided.

Another source of infection can come from drinking unpasteurised milk, although if you are producing and selling unpasteurised milk it will have undergone rigorous laboratory testing for safety. Bites from ticks can also be a source if the tick has previously been a parasite on an infected animal and skin abrasions from infected areas can also be at risk.

A well ventilated and thoroughly clean animal environment should virtually eliminate the risk of this disease.

RINGWORM

Ringworm is a fungus. It infects all livestock and pets from time to time and is easily contracted by humans. Broken skin is required for the fungus to enter, but it can live on walls, fences and gateposts for many years and also handling equipment such as head collars and saddlery.

It is 'self limiting' and will clear up in around six months, but the harm it causes along the way is so bad that it must not be ignored. Humans will usually contract it on their hands and arms, head and neck. The lesions caused are round and crusty, often developing into a large mass as several lesions conjoin. It is easily treated but must not be ignored.

Good hygiene on your holding should keep it at bay and creosoting woodwork or spraying regularly with a preparation such as Virkon S will control it well.

Keep infected livestock away from others and treat immediately, keeping a watchful eye on other animals and indeed yourself for any sign of infection. It normally takes 10 days from contact to signs of lesions.

SALMONELLA

Although most of us associate Salmonella with having 'eaten something,' in the case of us smallholders it can be caused by contact with that old favourite - farm dung.

This bacterium can be carried by most types of farm anima, so the risks to us are the same as the previous conditions and it can be avoided by our old friend hand washing. Never eat anything or smoke without having washed your hands. Remember that it can also be passed by hand to hand contamination and off loo door handles and flush handles, for instance when the previous occupant has not observed good hygiene.

In most cases salmonella infection consists of diarrhoea, fever and abdominal pains in humans, but it can have far reaching results and become very serious.

SCRAPIE

This affects sheep and goats and the precautionary measures for goat and sheep keepers are the same as for those who keep cattle as it is a similar condition to BSE.

SO, SHOULD WE BE CONCERNED?

The answer to this is no, not really, but we should be concerning ourselves with the way we conduct ourselves around our animals and our own hygiene with regard to eating and drinking around animals and, of course, HAND WASHING, but remember that a bar of soap can be one of the worst contaminants on your holding. Use a liquid soap in preference. Many bacterium loaded hands have used the soap before and this in itself can be a vehicle for infection. Use paper towels too to dry your hands if possible. Towels quickly become damp and dirty as not everyone will do a proper job in the washing department.

Keep your animals as clean as you can and keep pens regularly cleaned out and disinfected as appropriate.

Keep a special eye on small children and those who are not used to your farm environment as their immunity to these infections will be lower than yours. And don't let pregnant women into birthing areas or help with sick animals.

Above all, don't feel frightened by these conditions. The very fact that you are aware of them will safeguard your family and yourself. In over fifty years of animal husbandry I have not actually suffered with any zoonoses and, although one of my children once had a minor case of ringworm caught from a Guinea Pig, I have only ever known one person to become ill as a direct result of caring for livestock and they made a full recovery.

So enjoy your goats. Be responsible and caring and you will have many years of pleasure from them.

A SMALLHOLDER'S CHEESE

A SIMPLE RECIPE FOR THE DOMESTIC KITCHEN

I feel that it is important to remind you that these products must ONLY be used by you and your immediate family. It is illegal to sell or give either goat's milk or goat's milk products away without formal permissions from the various agencies involved. This could possibly be worthwhile even if you only have a couple of milking goats. This recipe will make a really lovely goat's cheese that you and your family will enjoy and should you decide to 'go commercial' it will set you in good stead for developing cheeses of your own.

SHOULD I 'PASTEURISE' MY GOAT'S MILK FOR CHEESE MAKING?

Pasteurisation is a way of sterilizing your goat's milk to ensure there is no risk of infection to those that consume it. This can vary from Ecoli infection through to a host of other problems. Historically, people have drunk goats milk through the ages without heat treatment. Most commercial goat farms pasteurise their milk in the same way as cows' milk but for small scale home production it is do-able at home on the stove. There is no doubt that heat treating any milk not only changes its flavour but also changes the enzymes within it and so for some people heat treatment is not a consideration at any cost. We (my family) have always drunk unpasteurised goat's milk and made unpasteurised goat's milk products and indeed 'went commercial' with unpasteurised goat's milk products after a fight with the Authorities, but got there in the end.

The key is to be scrupulously clean in the milking and after handling process. That way it is perfectly safe to drink 'raw' milk. However, if you are in any doubt at all about the standards you can achieve then heat treating your milk is essential.

HOW TO PASTEURISE

You will need:

- A large saucepan or preserving pan - stainless steel or enamel - with a lid, NOT aluminium or copper.
- A very fine stainless steel sieve or a colander and filter paper or sterilised muslin cloth.
- A floating dairy thermometer (around £10 each from smallholder supply shops) or jam thermometer.
- A clean sink full of very cold water and ice cubes.

METHOD 1

Strain your hygienically milked goat's milk into the preserving pan through the fine sieve or filter paper/muslin to remove any tiny debris such as hairs and dust (you might be surprised at what you find!)

Bring the milk up to between 63 and 66°C using your sterilised thermometer. Hold the temperature for 30 minutes, then cover and immediately remove from the heat and plunge into the cold water.

METHOD 2

Heat the milk as before to 72°C and hold for 20 seconds then cool as before and continue as below.

Leave the thermometer in situ and watch the temperature as it falls. As soon as it reaches 10°C, start to fill your containers for the fridge or freezer with a sterilised jug dipped into the milk. It's as simple as that. The key to success is to bring the temperature down as quickly as possible to ensure any bacteria does not begin to multiply.

CHEESE

Centuries ago, cheese was developed as a way to store milk for winter use. As far back as the Iron age, people were making and storing cheese in the UK.

RAISING GOATS

Goat's cheese can be made to any regional variation, just the same as cow's cheese. Fat content, breed of goat and all the other stuff that people might fire at you is complete nonsense. You CAN make goat's milk into a wide variety of cheeses.

THE SMALLHOLDER'S GOAT'S CHEESE
- finished weight between 1.5 & 2kgs.

INGREDIENTS:

- 3 gallons (24 pints) strained/filtered goat's milk-pasteurised or raw
- Cheese starter (available from smallholder supply shops or online)- try to get the sort that you add directly to the milk. Store in a freezer in between batches of cheese
- Rennet
- Salt
- Lard or 'Trex' white fat for preserving-approx 2oz

UTENSILS:

- 3 gallon preserving pan - stainless steel or enamel
- Pallet knife
- Cheese cloth or old clean sheeting or pillowcase cut up
- A plastic mushroom box or similar which will sit across the span of your kitchen sink
- Clean kitchen sink with no animals, meat, fruit or vegetables on the worktop!!
- A cheese mould/press or a new, large plastic flower pot with round holes in the bottom
- A heavy weight or weights giving a cumulative weight of around 2kg. (I use some rocks from my local beach but you will have some ingenious object to use, I'm sure. Whatever it is, wrap it in cling film or a plastic bag)

ALL UTENSILS MUST BE STERILISED OR PUT THROUGH THE HOT CYCLE OF YOUR DISHWASHER BEFORE USE - my poor dishwasher has seen some varied objects pass through its door, but I guess it relieves the boredom for the poor thing.

METHOD

Put the milk into the preserving pan and adjust the temperature by cooling or raising the temperature to 29°C. (Freshly milked goat's milk is pretty close to this temperature).

Add the cheese starter according to instructions for the quantity of milk used.

Add the rennet (2ml for every gallon of milk). Stir this thoroughly through the milk for a few seconds, no longer or the milk will form small curds and we need to produce large ones.

Cover the pan and keep warm until a firm curd has formed. This will generally take about one hour.

Now it gets exciting!

Take your pallet knife and carefully cut this now solidified curd both ways and across laterally as far down the pan as you can manage. There is a special tool known as a curd knife to do this with, but for domestic use a pallet knife does the job perfectly well.

Now raise the temperature of the curd on your cooker to 32°C. Do this VERY slowly taking about 30 minutes to reach the temperature. You need to be around for this bit as you will need to very gently stir throughout this process. Take care not to break up the curds below ½ inch in diameter.

Now remove from the heat source and place on your draining board and carefully begin to tip the whey off into another container. (This process is known as 'drawing the whey'). You will need to gently tip the vessel from one side to another to do this without the curd falling out. Using a colander (sterilised) to catch any odd bits is a good idea.

Eventually you will have drained the majority of the whey from the curds.

Now take your holey plastic box and line with the cloth you are going to use which has been rinsed in boiling water.

RAISING GOATS

Tip the curds and remaining whey into this and allow to drain for a further hour or so. Then cut the curds in this again. Sprinkle with approximately a tablespoon of salt and you will find that more whey will be generated.

Move the cloth around and the whey will be released again. This whey is going to go down the drain unless you can devise a way to catch it. It can be fed to pigs, used in baking and best of all for a type of bread known as whey bread. You can freeze your collected whey for future use.

So now your curds are going to be quite small and fairly dry and this is the time to pack them into a mould for shaping into your cheese.

You can use the flowerpot method which I still employ and used for several of my cheeses, even when I went commercial! If the flowerpot has been through the dishwasher, it can be a recycled one, not new by the way.

Line the flower pot with some more cloth (scalded again) and spoon the curd into it, pressing it down as you go. (Sprinkle some more salt onto the curds as you pack them, but no more than another tablespoon throughout. Salt is a necessary part of cheese making, not only to bring out the flavour but to help the preservation process). The curds from three gallons of milk will almost fill this to the top but over a period of hours this will settle and produce a 4 or 5 inch slab. Cover the mould with another cloth while you wait for this to happen.

Next turn out onto another piece of cloth or muslin and then invert the slab back into the pot/mould again. Now apply the weight to start pressing the cheese.

You will need to turn the cheese out daily into another clean cloth and repeat the inverting and pressing process for another 2 days.

Finally, grease the now well formed cheese with the lard or Trex, or even butter, wrap it again in another clean cloth quite tightly and set in a cool place for 4 to 6 weeks. Turn the cheese over every day during this time.

Although this cheese is ready to eat after 4 to 6 weeks, you can store it for 6 months or more to make a more mature product, but I'll bet you won't be able to wait!

Like all goat's products, cheese freezes well and can be kept for a very long time if you want to arrest its ripening process. Once thawed, the maturing process will begin again like magic!

WATCHPOINTS

Do not make bread or yeast products in the same room at the same time as preparing your cheese-yeast 'infects' cheese and makes it go bad. Meat products in close proximity can introduce unwanted and damaging bacteria to the cheese in the preparation process. Fresh fruit can also have yeasts on its surface and should be removed from the cheese production room.

NB. Natural yeasts are all around us and so easily inhabit a cheese. The key to success is good hygiene (AGAIN!)

References and Contact Information

British Goat Society
34-36 Fore street, Bovey Tracey, Newton Abbot, Devon TQ13 9AD
Tel:01626 833168 www.allgoats.com & www.allgoats.org.uk
Email: secretary@allgoats.com

Anglo Nubian Breed Society
4 Wadehouse Lane, Drax Hales, Selby, North Yorkshire YO8 8PN
Tel: 01757 618756
No website

British Alpine Breed Society
The Old Tanyard, Pound Hill. Corsham, Wiltshire SN13 9HT
Tel: 01249 716350
www.britishalpines.co.uk

British Boer Goat Society
Harperley View Harperley, Stanley, Co.Durham, DH9 9UB
Tel:01207 281550
www.britishboergoatsociety.co.uk

British Saanen Breed Society
Rouval, Ipswich road, Langham, Colchester, Essex, C)4 5NG
Tel: 01206 230756

British Toggenburg Society
Westward, Faversham Road, Wychling, Kent, ME9 0DH
Tel: 01795 886202

English Goat Breeders Association
Ivy Cottage, Whitchurch Lane, Oving, Aylesbury, Bucks. HP22 4EU
Tel:01296 640842

Golden Guernsey Goat Society
Yonder Cottage, Hugglers Hole,Semley, Shaftesbury, Dorset, SP7 9HG
Tel: 01747 851524
www.goldenguernseygoat.org.uk

Saanen Breed Society
Lindbrook Farm, Lindway Lane, Brackenfield, Derbyshire. DE55 6DA
www.saanenbreedsociety.org.uk

British Angora Goat Society
5 The Langlands, Hampton Lucy, Warwick,Warwickshire. CV35 8BN
www.britishangoragoats.org.uk

SPINNING

The Natural Fibre Company
Pipers Court, Pennygillam Way, Launceston, Cornwall PL15 7PJ
Tel: 01566 777635
Email: enquiries@blackerdesigns.co.uk
www.thenaturalfibre.co.uk

CURING AND DRESSING OF SKINS

Devonia Products,
Mardle Way, Buckfastleigh, Devon. TQ11 0AG
Tel: 01364 643355
No website

TAGGING AND TAGGING EQUIPMENT

Fearings
Creaton road, Brixworth, Northampton. NN6 9BW
Tel: 0845 600 9070
www.fearing.co.uk

Food Standards Agency
Tel: 0207 276 8000
www.food.gov.uk

Rural Payments Agency (CPH numbers)
0845 603 7777

Defra Helpline
0845 9335577
www.defra.gov.uk

Animal Health Information Line
0844 8844600

The Good Life Press
PO Box 536
Preston
PR2 9ZY
01772 652693

The Good Life Press Ltd. is a family run business specialising in publishing a wide range of titles for the smallholder, 'goodlifer' and farmer. We also publish **Home Farmer,** the monthly magazine for anyone who wants to grab a slice of the good life - whether they live in the country or the city. Other titles of interest:

A Guide to Traditional Pig Keeping by Carol Harris
An Introduction to Keeping Cattle by Peter King
An Introduction to Keeping Sheep by J. Upton/D. Soden
Build It! by Joe Jacobs
Building Fences and Gates by Andy Radford
Craft Cider Making by Andrew Lea
First Buy a Field by Rosamund Young
Flowerpot Farming by Jayne Neville
Grow and Cook by Brian Tucker
How to Butcher Livestock and Game by Paul Peacock
Making Country Wines, Ales and Cordials by Brian Tucker
Making Jams and Preserves by Diana Sutton
Precycle! by Paul Peacock
Raising Chickens for Eggs and Meat by Mike Woolnough
Showing Sheep by Sue Kendrick
Talking Sheepdogs by Derek Scrimgeour
The Bread and Butter Book by Diana Sutton
The Cheese Making Book by Paul Peacock
The Frugal Life by Piper Terrett
The Medicine Garden by Rachel Corby
The Pocket Guide to Wild Food by Paul Peacock
The Polytunnel Companion by Jayne Neville
The Sausage Book by Paul Peacock
The Secret Life of Cows by Rosamund Young
The Shepherd's Pup (DVD) with Derek Scrimgeour
The Smoking and Curing Book by Paul Peacock
The Urban Farmer's Handbook by Paul Peacock

www.goodlifepress.co.uk
www.homefarmer.co.uk